MISTER BARNEY FORD

A Portrait in Bistre

FORBES PARKHILL

Author of

Flyers of Fortune
Troopers West
Wildest of The West
The Law Goes West
Last of The Indian Wars
Mister Barney Ford

Editor of

The Wayward Horseman

MISTER
BARNEY FORD

A Portrait in Bistre

FORBES PARKHILL

SAGE BOOKS
DENVER

Sage Books are published by

Alan Swallow, 2679 South York Street, Denver, Colorado 80210

ILLUSTRATIONS

ACKNOWLEDGMENTS

The author expresses his gratitude to the following for their assistance in gathering material for this book:

Alys H. Freeze, head of the Western History Department, Denver Public Library; her predecessor, Ina T. Aulls; staff member Opal Harber; Pauline Robinson, Cosmopolitan Branch, and Sylva Tanberg, Genealogy Division.

Agnes Wright Spring, Colorado State Historian and Dolores C. Renze, Colorado State Archivist.

Eulalia D. Chapman, former director, Rocky Mountain Bibliographical Center, Denver.

Floyd F. Miles, librarian, Colorado State Supreme Court, Denver.

Mary Elizabeth Cody, historian, Wyoming State Historical Society, Cheyenne, Wyoming.

Helen Anderson, former director of publications, School District No. 1, Denver.

W. F. Dyde, University of Colorado, Boulder, Colorado.

Thomas Hornsby Ferril, Siewers Fincher, Dr. Clarence Holmes, all of Denver, and William S. Jackson, former Justice, Colorado Supreme Court.

Charles Bradley, Mrs. Lille Murphy, Lottie Porter, Helen Rich, Ed T. Stuard, all of Breckenridge, Colorado.

Robert A. Theobald of Leadville, Colorado.

Drs. V. B. Spratlin and Stanton L. Wormley, both of Washington, D. C.

The late Robert G. Seymour of San Francisco.

I

Barney was a little colored boy whose mother, Phoebe, was a slave housemaid at the Big House. Her hair was kinky and her skin almost crow-black, but his skin was so light an olive that it showed sunburn, and his eyes were blue-hazel and his hair a wavy chestnut. In the South before the war almost every plantation had one or more half-white youngsters underfoot.

Never having attended school, Barney was unable to read even three-letter words; had never held a book in his hands until the summer night that his mother whipped him so unmercifully.

In those days the Black Laws of the Carolinas and some other states of the South prohibited teaching a slave to read or write, under penalty of a fine of one hundred dollars or six months in jail, or both.

Although Phoebe was unable to read, she took the notion that if her little half-white boy could learn to read, he might not be forced to remain a slave when he was grown.

That was the reason she stole the dictionary from the Big House library. Another house servant had informed her that it contained "all the words in the world," and sometimes she had seen Claiborne, the young master, refer to it. To her way of thinking, that fat book represented the key to all knowledge.

The barefoot Barney disliked to quit playing bean bag with the other youngsters when she called him out of the moonlight into the slave cabin and drew the latch-thong inside and hung gunny-sacks over the two windows so no one would know of the terrible thing she was about to do.

Grasping a willow switch in one hand, she placed the tallow-

7

dip candle on the dirt floor, squatted, opened the dictionary and spread it out. Gripping the boy by the neck, she forced his eyes close to the open pages.

"Say me a reading word, child." Her harsh words left Barney frightened and trembling. "All the words in the world, they in that book. You got to learn them reading words, boy. Got to!"

He whimpered, for these were the first printed pages he had ever seen. "Can't say 'em, mama. Can't say 'em."

"I 'low I make you say 'em, boy!" Savagely she cut down with the switch across his bare legs. The sting brought tears to his eyes and a sob welled up from deep down in his throat. Tears made his nose run, and he wiped it with the back of a forearm. It was straighter than Phoebe's and less broad.

Both Barney and his mother were mystified by those mysterious little print marks on the page, for neither was aware that one must learn his letters before he can read words.

Exasperated, she seized him by the collar and slashed his legs with her willow switch until his bare olive calves were criss-crossed with great red welts and he lay kicking and squalling on the dirt floor.

Her tantrum subsiding abruptly, she dropped the switch and snatched up the sobbing child, cradling his head on her bony shoulder as she rocked back and forth on the floor, patting him on the back and moaning.

"My po' little Barney boy! Po' little Barney boy! Mama want to he'p him, but she don't know how."

All the rest of his days he was to remember those choking, despairing words. Even when he had become rich and famous, helping to make history, making and unmaking governors and senators and when they called him a president-maker; even then he could never forget.

"Mama want to he'p him, but she don't know how." Perhaps the words had something to do with the remarkable accomplishments of the grown Barney.

After a little, when his sobbing had dwindled off to sniffling, she took him by the hand and led him outside the cabin and sat him on the bench beside her. The bean bag game had ceased. The field hands and a few of the house servants were gathered about the slave cabins in little groups. A banjo was playing and a mournful, lonesome voice was singing softly, *Sometimes I'm up, Sometimes I'm down.* Unmindful of chigger bites, some field hands were sprawled out in the cool grass, weary after toiling all day in the cotton fields.

Through the gum trees, back from the river, the lights of the Big House windows glowed. But Phoebe was looking the other way, black finger pointing down by the stables behind the gin house and baling press where a huge cotton snatcher, Willie Joe, was treating a collar gall on a sore-back mule. The animal's name was Barney, and there had been a time when the little colored boy believed himself to be named for the mule.

"Looky there, boy. Willie Joe, he all wearied down from stoop work all day long. Willie Joe, he just like that old mule. Yo' mama, she don't crave for her Barney boy to grow up to be like old mule."

Barney had no wish to be a mule, but could not have told why, precisely, for the field hands worked quite as hard as the animal.

"Willie Joe got no more learning in his head than that no-'count mule. Both together, they don't know nothing. Less'n you got learning, boy, all your life you be no-'count like Willie Joe and old mule. Yo' mama ain't fixing to bring you up thataway, can she he'p it."

Shifting about, she pointed toward the Big House, where a carriage was drawing up at the portico and the young master, tall, graceful and handsome in his white linens, was welcoming his guests with outstretched hand.

"Son, what make young master different from Willie Joe? Answer me that."

Unlearned as he was, Barney was no simpleton. Young Claiborne was white and the field hand black. The whites were masters and owned the slaves and mules. To a child of eight, accepting life as he found it, it was that simple.

Countless others older and more learned than he, blacks and whites alike, would have reasoned the same, but before he could reply, his mother was answering her own question in a tumbling torrent of words.

9

"Young master, he got learning in his head! That's the answer. Boy, you got to get learning in your head. Got to know things. Get learning in your head, you never have to work in cotton fields like wearied-down old mule; some day you stand on gallery like young master, white folks call you *Mister*."

Barney was wondering if his mother actually believed that the difference between master and slave lay, not in the color of their skins, but in some inner quality, something that even a slave boy might acquire if only he knew how to go about it.

Now and then for some days he considered it when not chasing butterflies or making mud pies with a broken spoon, and might have forgot it except that his mother could never forget, and so persisted in trying to do something about it. As for Barney, as yet he was unable to cope with abstractions.

Quite naturally every slave resented his servitude, but with few exceptions all accepted it as they accepted illness and death; as the will of the Lord. Rare was the one with sufficient spirit to grapple with the seeming impossible and attempt to better himself; or, like Phoebe, to better their children. The first step was to learn to read, write, spell.

By means of the slave-quarters grapevine Phoebe learned of a house servant on an adjoining plantation who owned a spelling book and had taught himself to read fairly well, so several nights each week she led Barney across the fields and through the brakes where the panthers squalled, to the cabin where he could acquire the rudiments of learning.

The spelling book contained pictures that made the words easier to learn; dog, cat, apple, ox, and included the verses of the singing alphabet. It was far easier for the boy to learn his ABC's by singing them, like "A is for Apple," but it was almost a year before he could sing the alphabet through to "Z is for Zebra."

He had much rather been out playing bean bag than cramming his head with things that made no sense to him at the time, but always there was Phoebe with her willow switch to keep him at it. Except for that switch and the fierce mother-love behind it, certainly Barney never would have managed to subjugate the alphabet.

Presently, however, he found himself capable of mastering entire sentences from a hymn book Phoebe had stolen for him. She purloined a copy of *Ewell's Medical Companion,* which challenged him with considerably more formidable reading; long, exquisite, lilting words like *erysipelas,* that meant nothing to him but sounded musical and scholarly and gratifying. He delighted in rolling those melodious polysyllables over his tongue, and as for his mother, she was as exalted as if he were declaiming from a pulpit.

In due time, when he actually began to derive meaning from his sentences, he developed a vainglorious feeling of superiority because he was becoming more learned than she. He was acquiring an interest in learning, largely because it afforded him a means to show off, but when Phoebe found him flaunting his erudition before the other plantation youngsters she took the switch to him again, stricken with panic for fear the whites would guess the audacious, fearful plan that gradually was shaping itself in her mind.

Years later when he was admired and envied because of his wealth and of his influence in public affairs, he liked to say, "All I know is what my mother whipped into me," although the statement at best was but a half-truth.

She whipped him into getting started with his letters, and for a time the showoff in him kept him at it, but at length he found himself acquiring an interest in reading for another reason. Bit by bit, those printed sentences were leading him into a surprising and delightful new world beyond the ken of an ordinary unlettered slave boy. He was developing a mounting curiosity to know more and more.

When ten years old, almost sturdy enough to begin work in the fields, his spelling-book mentor loaned him a frayed and smudged copy of the anti-slavery newspaper, the *Liberator.* He read every word of it, and was amazed to learn that there were many — even whites — who did not agree that slavery was a system ordained of God. Illogical as it seemed to the slave boy, there actually were countless whites who held to the belief that all human beings were entitled to the same rights and freedoms.

The spelling-book man had taught Barney virtually everything of which he was capable, for his education fell short of the practice of chirography. So the boy taught himself to copy printed letters. Using a strip of peeled sycamore bark in place of slate or paper, he copied a scorching anti-slavery editorial by William Lloyd Garrison, a founder of the Anti-slavery Society, but when he proudly exhibited it to his mother, she destroyed it for fear it might fall into white hands and bring retribution upon him.

Up to this time Barney had been developing a form of intellectual snobbery, looking down on Phoebe because of her literacy lack, but the Garrison editorial effectively deflated him, leaving him with vastly more respect for her judgment, for the great man held, as did she, that only through learning could the black man achieve equality.

Now the mulatto boy's nebulous dreams were beginning to shape themselves into realistic hopes. Some day he might be free, free to come and go as he chose, free to earn his own way, to work for wages, to make something of his life by his own efforts.

He was eleven years old before he knew when or where he was born. That he might not forget, Phoebe made him pencil it down in a little blank book she had stolen for him. His printed note read: *Born January 22 at Stafford Court House, Virginia*, but it failed to include the name of his father, perhaps because it never occurred to him to ask. But he did learn how he came to be in Carolina rather than in Virginia, where he was born.

The "old master" — Claiborne's father — died soon after Barney's birth and his widow, "Old Missy," with her slaves and all her other property and possessions moved back to her own family home in Carolina. In his early forties at the time of his death, her husband had been known as the "old master" merely to distinguish him from his son, Claiborne, the "young master." Among the slaves quite naturally the widow, although still in her thirties at the time of the move, was called, but not to her face, "Old Missy."

As long as Barney could remember, the young master had managed the Carolina plantation, although Phoebe told him Old Missy actually owned it.

By and large, Claiborne's slaves held themselves to be fortunate, regarding him with respect and even affection. The *Liberator* editorials condemned floggings, which were fairly common on the neighboring plantations, but not here under the young master.

Slaves were bought and slaves were sold, but Old Missy would never approve breaking up a family.

The older black folk reported that handsome young Claiborne was moulded in the image of the old master. His erect carriage made him appear taller than his actual height. His cheeks were almost rose-petal pink, and with his wavy brown hair and hazel eyes he set many a feminine heart aflutter and by the hopeful mothers of the neighboring belles was regarded as quite a catch.

Claiborne's ready, engaging smile and his polished manners called to Barney's mind the story-book pictures of plumed knights. The young master was in his element when entertaining guests at the Big House. He was a graceful and accomplished dancer and was reputed to know all there was to know about horseflesh and womenfolk.

The worst that anyone could say about him was that he was indolent, but considering his rearing, with servants to attend his every want, that was to be expected.

Barney liked the young master and looked up to him and of course, in a distant, hopeless way, envied him. Sometimes, regarding from from a distance as Claiborne sipped his julep on the gallery with his guests, the slave boy reasoned that Phoebe must be mildly unbalanced to intimate that learning alone might enable her mulatto son some day to stand on a gallery like Claiborne while the whites called him *Mister*. About as likely as if she had predicted for him a plantation on the moon!

By the time he was fifteen Barney was beginning to fill out, nearly of an age to take his place in the cotton fields, and because of all his reading, the prospect left him less than overjoyed. Still on the skinny side, lacking the bulging muscles of the other black boys, he hoped vaguely to be chosen for a house servant. Besides being less arduous than field work, house work held forth the opportunity to steal books from the library to continue his surreptitious reading.

But the day came when Phoebe let him know that the young master had ordered that he was to begin work in the fields on his next birthday. Downhearted and miserable, he could not understand her lack of resentment. Rather than feeling disturbed, strange to say she seemed to cherish a feeling of relief.

He received the order with a sinking heart and a dark scowl.

"Don't want to snatch cotton, mama."

She made him stand up, scanning him from head to foot, intently studying the smooth ivory-tan of his cheeks. A strange look of distress appeared in her black eyes, and she cast a frightened glance over her shoulder.

"Got to go to the fields, boy. Got to go." Her voice sank to an apprehensive whisper. "Don't ever go near the Big House any more. Not ever." She gripped his shoulder, calloused black fingers sinking deep into his flesh, so that he sought to squirm away. "Don't ever go near Old Missy, Barney boy. She fixing to do you bad. You mind what I say?"

II

As he bent beneath the rows, thrusting the white cotton bolls into the bag trailing from his shoulder, Barney often wondered why his mother had warned him away from Old Missy and the Big House. He detested the back-breaking labor, but what actually depressed him was something within, something deeper than aching muscles. Was this a sample of what the remainder of his life was to be; year after year of stooping and snatching until he became as hopelessly apathetic as the sore-back mule?

The prospect seemed to leave the other youths unaffected, undismayed, but Phoebe had whipped a different something into Barney. The young alphabetarian had acquired sufficient learning to lead him to yearn for more; enough to stir his imagination; to give him notions. Readily enough he could exchange jibes and banter with the field hands, but he was oppressed by frequent periods of moroseness, experiencing bitterness and resentment that his stolid, untaught companions could never know.

Worst of all, the unaccustomed labor left him exhausted of an evening, too utterly weary to open a book. He was heavier than his mother now; not so tall, but sturdy enough that she no longer resorted to the use of her switch. But she kept scolding him to nose into the books she stole for him, and in the end the lash of her tongue proved more effective than the switch.

His sporadic study would have been less arduous had she not stolen one of Claiborne's old school books, an arithmetic. Now, "reading" books seduced his interest, stirred his imagination, left him athirst for more, but "ciphering" — that was another matter. The tables of figures left him cold, uninterested, for he could see no point in it all. Two times eight is sixteen. All right; what of it?

Occasionally when his mother was taken down with a spell of sore knees Old Missy sent her back to the cabin to rest on her rope-spring bed. Old Missy was indulgent with her help; thoughtful and kind. So Phoebe was laid up again that fateful day that the overseer sent word that Old Missy wished to see Barney at the Big House.

Because of his mother's warning he felt mildly apprehensive at first, but presently persuaded himself that perhaps this was his opportunity to be assigned to housework, so his doubts departed and he was all eagerness to hear the good news.

Quitting work in mid-afternoon, he washed his face and hands at the horse trough, combed his wavy hair and marched up to the gallery steps with flop-brim hat in his hands, respectful and humble.

Old Missy was seated on the gallery in a cane rocker, fanning herself with a lacy, hand-painted fan. Standing on the second step, Barney thought she appeared almost majestic sitting there in her flowered crinoline, hair untouched with grey; appeared materially younger than her forty-odd years. Her figure was still trim, her cheeks still touched with the bloom of youth.

"Well, well, Barney, so you're getting to be a big boy, now." Her voice was peach-down soft, her smile disarmingly friendly. "Where in the world have you been keeping yourself? I can't recall seeing you about the house for ever so long."

"Working in the fiields, ma'am. Snatching cotton." His uncertainty was banished by her gentle, friendly smile. He squared his shoulders, ceased to shuffle his feet.

"How old are you now, Barney? Seventeen? Eighteen?"

"Just turned seventeen, please, ma'am."

"And handsome . . . handsome!" Her blue eyes were making a head-to-foot inventory. "Turn around, Barney, so I can see you from the side. . . . Um-m. Much too handsome to be wasted in the fields. Wouldn't you like to make a change?"

He was picturing himself resplendent in the livery of a house servant. "Yes'm, please, ma'am."

At the table tap of Old Missy's fan a colored maid appeared in the doorway.

" 'Lissa, run tell Claiborne I wish to see him."

She continued to appraise the young mulatto, after the manner of the young master judging a quarter horse.

"Seventeen!" The fan fluttered languidly alongside her cheek. "Almost a man. Let me see; you were born before we came to Carolina, weren't you?"

Barney bobbed his head. "Yes'm." Old Missy was gazing past him, past the row of gum trees, and he gained the impression that the set of her lips hardened just a bit.

Striding through the doorway came young Claiborne, lithe, graceful, smiling. "What is it, mother?" He ignored the slave boy.

Old Missy tapped her fingertips with her flipped-shut fan.

"I was just wondering, Claiborne, why Barney here was assigned to the fields."

The young master's brows cat-backed into an arch of surprise. "Why, don't you remember, mother? Phoebe told us he preferred field work. When it's at all possible I like to give our people some freedom of choice. Makes better workers."

"Quite right. I had forgotten." Open again, her fan was weaving back and forth, languidly, and she was scrutinizing her personable son with a discreetly discerning gaze. Presently she turned to inspect the slave boy with the same studied care. "Very well, Barney. We'll see what can be done. That's all."

The elated Barney hastened back to the cabin to tell his mother the good news. She heaved herself up on the side of her bed, the whites of her wide eyes a bit frightening, and a faint moan escaped her, perhaps because of the pain of her sore knees.

"How you know you going to the Big House to work? Speak up, boy."

"Old Missy just as good as say so." He felt as happy as a frisky 'possum.

"Old Missy!" Phoebe's words caught in her throat. "Didn't I done told you —" Barney thought it strange that she should be so disturbed. "What she say, boy? What she say?"

His memory retained impressions readily. After reading a passage once, for long afterward he could repeat it word for word, so it was no trouble for him to repeat every word that Old Missy

17

had spoken, but his mother, unsatisfied, gripped his arm and shook him forcibly.

"Say so ain't do so. Words just saying things. What she do, boy? What Old Missy do?"

He knew of nothing to excite her so visibly, but to please her he did his best to explain.

"Old Missy just set there and look at me a long time, and then she look at young master a long time, and her little old foot go tappity-tap."

"Oh, Lord!" Phoebe's cheeks went suddenly ash-grey and she raised her arms overhead as she was wont to do in camp meeting. "She know, O Lord, she know! Old Missy know now, Lord! Old Missy know!"

The bewildered Barney watched her slide from her bed to the dirt floor. Seemingly oblivious of her sore knees, she knelt, trembling hands clasped before her.

"Lord, Lord, have mercy on my weary soul! Save my po' little Barney boy, Lord! He'p him and save him, Lord, from Old Missy. He'p him, Lord, 'cause I try to he'p him, but I don't know how!"

The mystified youth could make no sense of her wild words, but he sidled over to place a comforting hand on her quivering, bony shoulder.

"Now, now, mama. What fret you? What for you carry on so?"

Flinging her arms about his knees, she clutched him close. "Lord, Lord, don't take my boy away! Don't let Old Missy do him bad, Lord. Don't let her take him away from he mama!" She nuzzled her black face on the thigh of his sweaty field jeans, choking and sobbing. "Her foot go tappity-tap. Old Missy know!"

He circled her shoulders with an arm and struggled to lift her back to the edge of the bed, but he was still disconcerted, unable to account for her outburst.

"Why you cry, mama? What Old Missy know?"

A full minute elapsed, and more, before she regained control of herself and her sobbing finally subsided. Although edging away from him, she still clung to his hand, and presently when words came they were tense and husky.

"She look at you, child, and she look at young master, and you

18

look so much alike that all at once she know what she never know befo'; that you both gotten the same papa. It come to her that old master, he yo' papa; that young master, Claiborne, he yo' very own half-brother. That what make her little old foot go tappity-tap."

Startled but not profoundly disturbed, he merely stood patting her shoulder in an awkward effort to reassure her.

Among its slaves, almost every plantation numbered one or more mulattoes, and generally it was assumed that they had been fathered by the white master. Barney knew a half-caste slave on a nearby plantation whose owner was his own white father. Such things happened; much, he supposed, as mules happen when horses and donkeys run in the same pasture.

For as long as he could remember he had been aware that his skin was lighter than that of the other slaves, but had wasted no thought on it. Nor did the other occupants of the slave cabins, so far as he could tell, for they were accustomed to accept the inevitable as the will of the Lord.

Sometimes he had wondered idly why no man ever lived in Phoebe's cabin, for men lived in the other cabins, but he never asked. On some plantations families were separated when slaves were sold. Husbands were taken away to the auction block and never came back. Sometimes wives, as well.

Taking his hand from his mother's shoulder, he stepped across the cabin to peer into the cracked mirror hanging from a nail in the wall. Out of doors the sun was sinking, but inside there remained sufficient light for him to study his reflection.

Yes, although he had never noticed it before, there seemed no doubt of the resemblance that Phoebe guessed Old Missy had noted. Claiborne's eyes were hazel, Barney's blue-hazel; the young master's skin was fair while the young slave's was ivory-tan; the white man was some years the older, but the conformation of the nose was the same, and the set of the jaw.

Both were slender, and when Barney got his growth they should be approximately the same height. Both moved with the same easy, graceful gait, each carried himself rigidly erect. Barney found himself wondering how he would look with his wavy hair neatly trimmed, standing on the gallery in a white suit, holding forth his hand to welcome guests who called him *Mister*. He laughed a little, for the thought seemed outlandish.

Turbulent thoughts were racing rampant through his cluttered mind. Now Old Missy knew him to be the son of her dead husband, his son by a black woman. But did Claiborne know? Had she told him? Would she tell him? Had he guessed?

Or, having guessed, had he merely dismissed it as the black folk dismissed it, as the will of the Lord? Certainly had Claiborne realized his relationship to the mulatto slave, he had never evidenced it by act or word.

Perhaps he did not know. And what did it matter, one way or the other? Barney liked and respected the young master, but cherished no brotherly affection for him. Why should Claiborne feel otherwise?

As he inspected his mirrored reflection he began to realize why, after Old Missy had compared the two, her little old foot had gone tappity-tap, but as yet he simply had not given a thought to how this new development might affect his own future.

"What fo' you grieve so, mama? Don't you want I should work at the Big House?"

Since Phoebe was seated on the edge of the bed, it scarce could have been her sore knees that led her to moan.

"Don't talk crazy, boy. You never going to work in Big House; not long as Old Missy live. What you think white folks say, they see young master and nigger boy look 'xactly alike? Do Old Missy think white folks know that old master, her husband, was papa of nigger boy, she die, likely.

"Old Missy, she don't want you around no mo'. She fixin' to do you bad." Her hands were covering her face, the tears leaking through her fingers. "O Lord, Lord, don't let 'em take my Barney boy away!"

Although uneasy, he still was unable to see why she should be so disturbed.

"She mad with you, mama? Old Missy mad with you 'cause old master my papa?"

"Not with me, son; not with me. Old master long time dead. Old Missy mad with you."

"With me? Why, mama? I don't do nothing to make her mad. Why Old Missy mad with me, mama?"

" 'Cause you is, child; 'cause you purely is." Oblivious of her ailing knees, she leaped from the bed, seized him and shook him. "You's got to run away, boy. You's got learning in your head. You can get along."

Barney was dumfounded. Run away? Certainly the thought had occurred to him now and then, as it had to every slave. Pleasant to dream about, but that was all.

"Run away? Don't know how, mama."

Well enough he knew the fate of runaway slaves, here in the Deep South. He knew of two who, captured, had been whipped until half dead and left with spirit forever broken. Such a prospect held no appeal.

One he knew who had not been recaptured. Had the runaway reached free soil he would have managed to send a message back to his family, but three years had elapsed without word from him. Barney could only guess his fate, but the guess was terrifying.

From reading the *Liberator* he was aware that many had won their way to freedom, but mostly they were from the border states, where escape was infinitely easier than here in Carolina.

Constantly the *Liberator* was urging freedom-loving slaves to consult agents of the Underground Railroad, but naturally it never identified these agents nor how they might be located. This a slave was supposed to learn by means of the grapevine.

But one never knew whom to trust. Everyone knew that perhaps a year of planning and saving must precede an actual break. Barney told himself that perhaps he would make the break ultimately, but right now he wholly lacked Phoebe's sense of urgency.

Here on the plantation he had known security and was treated leniently and life was far from unpleasant. Since his infancy he had never been more than a few miles from the slave cabins, and the prospect of running away into an unknown world terrified him. After all, he had done no wrong. Why should Old Missy wish to do him bad?

So he did nothing, and for some time nothing happened. Instead of being assigned to the Big House he remained working in the fields, and concluded that perhaps his mother was a bit touched for worrying so much about him.

One night after he had gone to bed his mother stole from the cabin and was absent all night, and he was not aware of it until she returned at sunrise, arms bramble-scratched, soaked and muddy from attempting to wade the river.

"I try to he'p you, son, but I don't know how." She was mired down in a slough of mental depression, which was unusual for her, and was moody and mean, and at first he failed to realize that she had been attempting to get in touch with an agent of the Underground.

But shortly her spirits rose, and instead of being mean she was angry at herself for her failure to find the agent, and her eyes seemed to bulge and her teeth gleamed white as she cried out in fierce desperation, "Next time I make it! Next time I find him and he he'p me to he'p you run away!"

Although Barney's reading had sparked a yearning for freedom and a better way of life, as yet he had done nothing about it. But bit by bit as his mind matured he was changing, and the responsible factor was the disclosure of his kinship to the young master.

Both were sons of the same father. Why then should the young master loll about in Big House luxury, free to do as he chose, with servants to wait on him, with an education at the university to bring him knowledge; with the legal right to own human beings and with all the good things of life provided for him by the product of their toil?

Why should this be so when Claiborne's mulatto half-brother was compelled to live in a slave cabin and labor in the cotton fields, forbidden by law to acquire schooling, forbidden to travel more than a few miles from the plantation without a written pass?

Was it the will of the Lord that of two sons of the same father, one should be the slave of the other? And if so, why? Why?

There had been a time when he had supposed it was because one's skin was white and the other's black. Did the Lord love white men better than black? Was it true that the descendants of Ham were accursed?

No, that could not be the answer. He knew enough of the law

to gather that when white mated with black, the children follow the condition of the mother. Black mother, black child. So, although his father had been white, Barney himself was a Negro.

But all the slaves knew of the mulatto in Charleston born of a white woman and hence, in the eyes of the law, considered white. He was a mulatto and Barney was a mulatto, but the Charleston man was freeborn and Barney was a slave. No, the difference between slave and freeborn was not in the color of the skin.

His mother had told him that the difference between the young master and her son was "learning in the head." Claiborne had attended the university, possessed learning. Barney had gained a modicum of learning — equivalent, perhaps, of a third grade schooling — but where did it get him? He still was a slave, had no valid reason to expect that he would not die a slave.

Suppose he continued to study diligently, acquiring more book-learning than Claiborne had gained at the university; would such an achievement make him the equal of his half-brother? So the whites would call him *Mister*? He knew damn well that it would not.

Then was Phoebe wrong? Had the Lord willed him, along with the sore-back mule, to remain the property of his own half-brother? If so, where was the need of studying, since learning alone could not solve his problem?

Why not accept his lot, and to hell with all this book learning? Would he not be happier in the end? He knew that many a slave lived a reasonably contented life despite his lot.

What if he followed his mother's advice and ran away? How could his reading help him? In the southern states the law barred a man of color from many occupations, and the free soil of the North seemed as far away as another planet.

In groping about for a solution to his bitterness he was forced to admit that it was beyond him. As Phoebe had wanted to help him, he wanted to help himself, but simply did not know how.

Could he learn? He did not know. Would the books tell him? They seemed to offer his only hope. Perhaps if he acquired sufficient learning he would find the answer.

Perhaps book learning would point the way to freedom, so

some day he could own a Big House of his own and the whites would call him *Mister* and both sons of his white father would be equal. He had just finished reading the dialogue between master and slave in the *Columbian Orator*.

He could not bring himself to hate Claiborne. Certainly it was no fault of the young master that one son of his father had been born white and the other black. But the bitterness sparked to life because he had been born the slave of his own half-brother never died out in Barney.

Again a few nights later Phoebe disappeared from the cabin, and he knew she was striving once more to find the Underground agent.

She never came back. They found her gaunt and ugly body on a mud flat, where it had washed up after she had drowned in her second attempt to cross the river.

The day after they laid her in the burying ground, Barney was sold to his new master.

III

When drunk, shrewd and massive Big Thompson could be downright mean and nasty. He could win friends with his kindly smile as easily as he made enemies with his overbearing ways and sharp business practices. Barney found him to be a reasonably well-meaning and kindly master.

At first the young mulatto slave was baffled by the strange rhetoric of his new owner. Reared in New England and educated at Bowdoin, Big Thompson favored esoteric quotations from the classics and sounded his R's like a foreigner.

As a young man he had put in a year at teaching, but being subject to a vagabond urge, joined a traveling troupe of actors. Mercenary instincts triumphing over his love of dramatics, he finally became a speculator, buying and selling whatever he might turn at a profit; hogs mostly, but likewise cattle and horses and cotton and slaves.

Barney had cost him five hundred and sixty dollars, but Big Thompson calculated that by the time the young mulatto got his growth he would bring easily twelve hundred, and meanwhile his other slave, old black Isaac, whose rheumatic knees were troubling him, needed a good, stout boy who was fast on his feet to help him handle the droves of wild Kentucky hogs.

Bachelor Big Thompson made his home at Columbus, Georgia, in a frame house on the piney grove hillside overlooking the whitewater stretch of the Chattahoochee River. Most of the time his trading expeditions took him away from Columbus, and while he was on the road the windows of the house and of the frame shack housing his two slaves were boarded up and the jimson weeds grew rank in the livestock pens.

Big Thompson's clean-shaven face was a veined and bloated red and his bald head was the shape of a squash, pinched across the brows and bulging at the jowls. He carried a walking stick with a gold head, using it mostly to slash at weeds when sober and at Barney when otherwise.

Oddly enough, during his bouts with John Barleycorn he would blister black Isaac with blasphemy, but never so much as laid a finger on the rheumatic old man. It soon became clear to Barney that the two loved each other like brothers, and that this torrent of abuse was merely evidence of the strange master's fondness for the black man who had served him faithfully for so many years.

Big Thompson possessed a noble belly, across which he wore a flowered waistcoat and a heavy gold watch chain. Barney would stare enviously as his owner toyed with the fat seal watch charm carven with an intaglio likeness of Aphrodite, and he resolved that if ever he became free and rich he would have just such a chain and charm.

Late of an afternoon, on the return to Columbus with a drove of Kentucky hogs, when old Isaac's knees were beginning to give out, the master would shout at him to get the hell into the surrey and take over the reins so the white owner could take a nap. This happened so frequently that Barney convinced himself that the actual reason Big Thompson had bought a boy was because he wished to ease the labors of the failing old black man.

As for Isaac, he cared for the wants of the white man as if the master were a helpless child. The aging slave no more would have run away to freedom than he would have deserted his church.

The first time Barney heard him singing that mellow old spiritual, "There's a better day a-coming, fare you well, fare you well," he was certain that Isaac was expressing the emancipation blues, but he speedily changed his mind.

At first Barney suspected that the old man was jealous of the new boy, fearing perhaps that the mulatto might replace him in the affections of the master, but as time wore on Isaac mellowed as his misgivings appeared groundless.

Barney was reasonably well satisfied with his lot under his new master, for he was seeing some of the world and meeting new people, and was becoming convinced that nursemaiding a drove of hogs 'cross country just can't be beat for a liberal education.

Had he remained on the Carolina plantation he might never have seen a United States Senator, much less elect one.

One advantage of hog droving, it improves the vocabulary, adding countless swear words that otherwise one might never learn. Returning to Columbus from a hog-buying trip into Kentucky, Isaac and Barney would trudge along in the dust behind the hogs, pelting them with clods and exhortations, while Big Thompson occupied the surrey in front of the drove, with his jug and his books.

One of these trips took them to Dahlonega, in the hills of northeast Georgia, where the entire community was excited over the discovery of gold near Auraria, a hamlet in Lumpkin County. Eager to try his hand at the placer mining, Big Thompson bought a claim near Auraria and set Isaac and Barney to work operating a sluice and rocker.

He did the hoping and they did the sweating, but none of the three possessed the slightest knowledge of placer mining. The adjoining claim was being worked by a group of Cherokee Indians who had remained behind when their tribe had been moved from Georgia to the Cherokee Nation, and from them the eager Barney learned much that was to prove of benefit in the gold rush days of later years.

Even though unable to share in the expected riches, he was fully as enthusiastic as his master at the prospect of discovering gold in the gravel bar. Up to this time he had been unaware of any means to acquire money except by working for wages or by trading, and such activities were largely monopolized by the whites.

But here on the nearby Singleton and Calhoun mining properties they were digging wealth right out of the ground. As he worked the rocker and watched Big Thompson eagerly inspect the samples for traces of color, his imagination almost carried him away.

He was wishing that he were free like his master, so he could keep what gold dust might be washed out. He was resolving that if ever he became a free man he would never waste his time working for day wages, but would find a gold bar and with its riches build himself a Big House of his own, where he could stand on the gallery like Claiborne and welcome guests and listen to them call him *Mister*. He was stricken with the gold fever and never managed to recover from it, suffering relapses all the rest of his days.

Sadly enough, they were expending a vast amount of muscular energy, but were finding no gold. Disgusted, Big Thompson attempted to sell his claim but failed, so he finally abandoned it to resume the hog business, in which one seldom gets rich but always manages to get along.

On their northbound trading trips there was seldom livestock to drive, so Isaac or Barney could drive the surrey while the master sat in the rear seat, turnip nose poked into one of his leather-bound books. Often as not, when the mood came to him, he would read aloud in a deep, empty-rain-barrel voice that left Barney in a hypnotic trance, for of course the youngster never before had listened to a professional actor.

Without effort Barney could remember these lines, for his memory was razor-sharp, whetted by his study from stolen books. Never having heard of Shakespeare or Milton, he was wholly ignorant of who had written the words he delighted so much to parrot; knew merely that they sounded musical and magnificent as he rolled them off his tongue after the manner of Big Thompson.

Barney's natural speech was the slurring, halting idiom of the Carolina plantation, but strangely enough he learned to imitate his master phonetically, so that once, showing off before a group of admiring colored girls at Frankfort, he astonished a listening white man who cried out, "My God, boy, where 'bouts did you learn to talk thataway? You sound like a god damned college professo'; like a professo' from the No'th!"

The time was to come when Barney was a candidate for public office, that he would make use of these quotations from the classics to the astonishment of his audiences, but his judgment may have been at fault, for it led some listeners to think him an upstart.

Now, although he could rattle off Shakespeare by the page, he was unable to write a word; not even his own name; merely copy printed letters.

In the absence of his mother's switch to spur him on, he had turned his back on the dull study of arithmetic. Perhaps it was due to mental laziness, but there was nothing of laziness when it came to reading books filched when Big Thompson was drunk. Reading helped him to escape from the dreariness of hog-tending and promised, somehow — he was quite hazy as to just how — ultimate deliverance from his physical bondage.

Many of the lengthy words in these leather-bound classics balked him, but he had never forgotten about the fat book containing "all the words in the world," so he traded one of the master's suckling pigs to a white schoolboy for a pocket dictionary, hid it in his bundle and used it to help him with the difficult ones.

He had heard and read about the Bible, but never saw a copy until he stole it when Big Thompson was sleeping off one of his spells. At the bottom of the first page he came upon a passage, Genesis 1:27, that left him uncertain and wondering for years to come:

So God created man in his own image . . .

So man was the image of God! His conception of God was rather hazy, but such as it was, it was cast in human form. Now he began to wonder. Was God white? Was He black? Or was He, like the Chinese, yellow?

He wished he could ask Big Thompson about it, but dared not. He was certain that he already knew what any white man would think. Could any white man possibly believe God to be anything but white?

But why? There it was, written down in black and white in the Bible. Was there not just as much reason to suppose that the black man reflects the image of God? Did Claiborne represent the true image of God? Or did Barney? And how about the Cherokee Indians in the Georgia gold fields?

His mind in confusion, he turned to Isaac for counsel as they trudged behind their hogs.

"God? Why, Barney, He white. Reckon everybody knowed that."

"But why? How you figure it, Isaac?"

The old man flung a clod at a laggard sow. " 'Cause why? Was God black, would He boon the white folks with all the good things, like He do? No! He'd set the black man free and see that they always have 'lasses for they bread."

Barney was unable to see it in that light. "Don't seem right and just, Isaac. People are different colors."

"You just an ignorant boy, Barney. The president, he a Whig, ain't he? So he don't pass out any jobs to the Democrats, do he? Well, then! Stands to reason God white, 'cause He do all His favors to the whites. Ever see a black angel or a black cherubim or a black seraphim? No! 'Cause God give all the best jobs to His own people. Just stands to reason, a pure natural fact."

The Democrats stood a chance to elect their own president and win all the government jobs, but how could black men elect a black God? Certainly it was madness to hope that a black man could ever be elected president. Barney failed to find the answer.

Back at Columbus after a swing through Kentucky, Big Thompson was easing his rheumatism in the rocking chair on the gallery of his frame house and Barney was out in the feeding pens slopping the hogs. In the two years that he had served the drover he had grown two inches, his muscles had hardened and his frame filled out.

Physically he was almost a man, and had developed a deep, rich baritone, which, however, failed to appeal to the finer sensibilities of the hogs, even when roaring forth the most persuasive profanity. Being hogs, they were scrabbling with their forefeet in the trough, and Barney was becoming exasperated.

Profanity failing, he drew upon his store of remembered quotations, and in an angry effort to shame them, called out, *"With eager feeding food doth choke the feeder."*

Behind him, Big Thompson brought his cane thumping down on the gallery floor and shouted, "Come here, boy! Hop!"

Though sober at the time, the master's peremptory shout left Barney thoroughly frightened as he hurried to the gallery, snatched off his battered straw hat and bleated, "Yes, sir."

"Where did you learn that, boy? Where did you learn to sound your R's? Damn your hide, I could close my eyes and swear I was listening to Henry Ward Beecher."

30

Fearing to disclose his ability to read by admitting that he had quoted from a book, he produced a hasty yet plausible lie. "Please, sir, master, listening to you."

"Don't lie to me, you saddle-colored reprobate!" Scowling angrily, Big Thompson shook the cane at him. "Tell me the truth now, or I'll skin you alive!"

Impudence was farthest from his mind, but the first thing that popped into Barney's head was, *"Fear not, my lord, your servant shall do so."*

"Good lovely Jehosaphat!" Rolling his eyes, the master clapped a hand to his brow. "A nigger boy spouting from *Midsummer Night's Dream!*" Thumping the floor with his cane, he was angry no longer, and bellowed out a great whoop of a laugh that allayed the youth's panic and brought a pert smile to his lips. "Go on, boy. Go on."

Here was an opportunity for Barney to show off. Striking a pose, he clowned the last line of:

> *"Present mirth hath present laughter;*
> *What's to come is still unsure."*

Big Thompson appeared to be on the verge of a stroke, his bald head reddening as he slapped his fat thigh and roared. Presently he calmed down and worked up a sly look, suspecting perhaps that Barney was making a fool of him. Calling Isaac, he made him swear that he knew that Barney had learned all these lines merely by listening to the master himself.

Even then he could scarcely believe it, and to test him, reeled off a difficult quotation he had learned in his Bowdoin days and never recited since, but Barney reeled off the quatrain of ten-syllable iambics right after him.

The drover was delighted to learn of his young slave's accomplishment and began to show him off before his white friends and win bets on him, and from time to time even took pains to teach him favorite passages. Boasting that he had taught Barney everything he knew, he took a vicarious pride in the exhibitions as indicating how well-read he himself must be, yet he never suspected that the young mulatto had got most of his quotations at first hand from stolen books. Sometimes when Barney reeled off an exceptional quotation, the master was uncertain who had originated it, Big Thompson or Shakespeare.

Although he never saw the inside of a schoolroom, in later years his precise enunciation and fund of quotations led Barney to be taken for a college graduate. He never ceased striving to improve his speech, but the years of his youth spent in imitating the former teacher and actor accounted, in part, for his cultivated diction and extensive vocabulary.

One quotation he kept to himself, never reciting it before a white man:

> *"Slaves who once conceive the glowing thoughts*
> *Of freedom, in that hope itself possess*
> *All that the contest calls for."*

Before long the railroad was built into Columbus and ruined Big Thompson's business, for it was cheaper to ship hogs by rail than to drive them across country. He set himself up as a cotton buyer, and no longer required two servants. He could manage well enough with only Isaac to serve him.

Barney was troubled, for he knew that slaves no better than he were bringing twelve hundred dollars or more on the New Orleans market, and he was well aware that his appetite was downright expensive.

Being a New Englander, Big Thompson should have been opposed to slavery, and for all anyone knew, perhaps he was. Probably he was like so many others ready to modify their beliefs for the sake of their pocketbooks. A shrewd businessman, he seldom was bested in a trade, and Barney was a twelve-hundred-dollar asset that was yielding no dividends, which is sufficient to break the heart of any businessman.

Still there remained means by which the young mulatto could be made to yield cash dividends. If an owner had no need for a slave he could rent out his services. This was known as "hiring his time."

The original master owned him, the man who hired his time

worked him. So Big Thompson hired Barney's time to the captain of the *Lulu Belle*, thus continuing to enjoy dividends from his asset.

The *Lulu Belle* was one of sixteen side-wheel steamboats moving cotton barges up and down the Chattahoochee between Colum-bus and Apalachicola Bay, on the Florida Gulf coast. Barney had been hired out as a cotton roustabout, but had no liking for the labor and set out to better himself by learning to shoot craps. He had everything to gain and literally nothing to lose.

Between trips he laid over at Big Thompson's place and persuaded Isaac to teach him to cook, for he was plotting to better his lot. During his sixth trip down the river he won the cook's job from him in a crap game, and the captain never discovered the difference until two trips later. As Barney was providing tastier meals than his predecessor, it was agreeable with everyone except, perhaps, the loser in the crap game.

Now Barney was a man past twenty-one, more and more yearning to be free. Doubtless this was because he had traveled more than most slaves, but more probably because he had learned to read and because his readings gave him notions.

What with reading and crap shooting, his education was progressing systematically, but the scope of his reading was becoming broader. He was unable to procure as many books as when Big Thompson and his library had been so readily available for covert borrowing, but here and there he could pick up more newspapers.

The *Liberator* editorials were proclaiming the new nation, Liberia, to be established in Africa for Negro freedmen from America. Barney indulged in much wishful dreaming about this new nation for his people, thinking how satisfying life in such a place would be; a place where there were no whites and he would be just as good as the next man. The world would be an ideal place if there were no whites and everyone addressed him as *Mister*.

With all his reading, his knowledge of geography was singularly limited. Actually he knew only that Africa lay far across the ocean.

He took to speculating as to means of making his way to Liberia, perhaps by stowing away on a ship, but was surprised to learn that there was no steamship service between Apalachicola Bay and Liberia. He decided that his best chance was to run away to the free soil of the North before making more definite plans to go to Liberia.

Meanwhile Big Thompson's rheumatism was troubling him more and more, his shoulders were becoming hunched, his fingers misshapen. His disposition was souring and he sought so much solace in the jug that he lost his job as cotton buyer, blaming his luck on the general contrariness of mankind and on the railroad that had forced him out of the hog business.

Barney was becoming uneasy, for constantly his master was grumbling, muttering about retiring and moving to St. Louis to live with a married sister. He could sell his younger slave for twelve hundred dollars, keep Isaac to serve him in his old age, and still retain a stake sufficient to keep him in whisky for the rest of his days. The lot of the worried Barney as a "hired time" cook was as pleasant as a slave could expect, and from day to day he lived in fear of being sold back into a cotton field.

But for all his grumbling and damning the railroad there was a soft streak in Big Thompson, and he could not bring himself to convert his mulatto asset into cash. Barney had been on the *Lulu Belle* more than two years when Big Thompson sold his Columbus home, loaded his two slaves in the surrey and headed for St. Louis.

Barney's fears vanished when he found himself hired out as cook on a New Orleans packet, a huge Mississippi side-wheeler, with gilt sun rays painted on its paddle boxes.

Now he had an opportunity to see more of the world, and moreover he had access to a library of books that he could read and no one the wiser, since the officers were too busy to read and most passengers preferred to watch the scenery, play poker or catch up on their romancing. And there were newspapers from St. Louis and New Orleans, so for the first time in his life he could pick and choose and not merely steal his reading matter at random.

Of course the wages that would have been paid him had he been a free man went to Big Thompson, but a "hired time" worker was permitted to keep his tips, largely because there was no means of keeping check on him. But since a cook seldom comes in direct contact with the passengers, optimistic Barney set out to win a waiter's job by shooting craps, but here on the Mississippi he found himself in fast company, competing with the world's most accomplished crap shooters, and he lasted about as long as it would take a white professional river gambler to fleece a victim.

So back at St. Louis after his first round trip he disclosed to Big Thompson his ambition to become a waiter. The old man damned him for an ungrateful nigger, but the next trip but one Barney found himself hired out as waiter on another packet, on the New Orleans-St. Louis-Louisville run.

Here he laid the foundation of the fortune he made in later years, when he was a bank director and wealthy, for within a year his tips came to more than twenty dollars. This was due in part to the fact that he was shrewd enough to keep out of the crap games, not that he had no wish to double his capital, but because he was sufficiently intelligent to realize that as yet he lacked the intellectual qualifications for this type of speculation.

Likewise, he was acquiring experience that was to prove of immeasurable help in later years when he was building and operating luxury hotels. He was learning that, although victuals are important, guests willingly pay for service.

He learned something, too, from a passenger intending to give him a kind word in place of a dime. From somewhere out of his book learning Barney recalled the quotation, " '*Tis nobleness to serve; help them who cannot help again.*"

The passenger's eyes widened as the mulatto waiter quoted Emerson and he left a generous tip. Thereafter Barney continued to show off his learning, and the policy paid in many additional dimes and quarters.

Strangely enough, in dealing with the white steamboat passengers he used the cultivated inflection that teacher-actor Big Thompson would have used, but in the company of those of his own race, for fear of being thought "uppity," he reverted to plain plantation-hand talk. He never ceased striving to improve his speech, for he was well aware how essential it was if ever the whites were to address him as *Mister*.

With all his book-learning, at the age of twenty-four he could write nothing but his own name, although he could copy printed letters. Conscious of his limitation, he bought a school copy book, the first of his unstolen books.

Across the top of each page in chirographic letters appeared some proverb, such as "Honesty is the best policy," or "A penny saved is a penny earned." Once he learned to identify the written with the printed letters he speedily mastered this, to him, fascinating new art.

About this time he encountered a passenger from Carolina whose body servant brought him his first news of the old plantation. Old Missy had married again and died, but her entire estate was left to Claiborne, who had married well and was expecting to enter politics.

Since he hoped to be free some day, Barney was fitting himself to make his own way in the world. He knew how to cook, to wait on table and to pan gold, which was more than most of his race knew, but he was weak on figures, sometimes making mistakes in adding a passenger's tab.

So he bought an arithmetic and taught himself to add and subtract and divide, but his mathematical education might have terminated there except for the science of crap shooting.

He was learning constantly by listening to those he served; bankers, cotton speculators, gamblers. The card sharps referred to themselves as "speculators," and were so listed in the early city directories. Win or lose, they were the most generous tippers and were accorded the best service by the waiters.

A young gentleman on his way to New Orleans to spend an inheritance was relieved of his funds by the river sharpers. He tried to laugh it off, but as Barney served the last round of bourbon he could see the young man's hands clenched in his lap.

"Son," the leading gambler magnanimously told the loser, "I'm going to give you a thousand dollars worth of free advice which you won't take. Speculating on how the cards will fall is not an art, but a science. Play hunches and you lose your shirt. It's purely a matter of mathematics, son; higher mathematics. You got to know the law of probabilities so you can take calculated risks. That's the only way you can beat this game, and even then there's a risk that you can't calculate, and that's whether the game's on the level."

It is safe to say that the young gentleman never took his thousand dollars worth of free advice, but Barney took it. It shed light on crap shooting as a science. Could he but master higher mathematics there was no limit to what he might accomplish with a pair of dice.

Immediately he began to interest himself in mathematics, now that he could see that it would advance his career. After he had gone back to his arithmetic and worked out a table showing the chances for and against throwing a seven he tried it out in a game behind the cotton bales on the landing, but it failed to work out the way he had expected and he lost seventy-eight cents.

He perceived the reason at once. A scientist would make an indifferent crap shooter if he knew only mathematics; it must be high mathematics, the higher the better. Algebra, even.

So he bought an algebra book and set himself to study the law of probabilities as applied to a pair of dice. But presently he forgot all about crap shooting, for he was discovering something vastly important, something that was to help him immeasurably in later years, bringing him the reputation of being a wizard. He discovered how to calculate the Unknown.

IV

Of the thousands of eminent scholars and philosophers study-ing matters of great import, all reached the conclusion that Life is a mystery and the Future a sealed book, but as Barney proved to his own satisfaction, all were wrong. It remained for him to prove how simple it is to cipher out the Unknown.

The river gambler based his system on the law of probabilities. The system Barney worked out is based on the law of positivities, of which he was the discoverer.

What does one wish to know that he doesn't know? How to get rich? In an algebra book Barney discovered how to get rich, and subsequently made more than one fortune.

What else does one wish to know? If war is coming? Barney worked that out in advance, too, and before many years the Civil War broke out; absolute proof that his system is actually effective.

These Unknowns that he could calculate in advance are simple examples, like those one finds in the beginning of the algebra book. Toward the back of the book are found the longer and harder prob-lems, but the answer to each one had been an Unknown until some intelligent fellow like Barney worked it out in the first place.

Naturally an algebra contains only a limited number of prob-lems. They merely show the student how to solve similar problems; to reason out more complicated Unknowns.

Within a year Barney had worked out the answers to countless problems that had been troubling mankind for generations. He was finding answers that no one else knew to big and important ques-tions. Already he was working on problems concerning God and the Hereafter that had baffled everyone else, including the preachers.

All this he was canny enough to keep strictly to himself, for should he intimate that he knew how to cipher himself into the Future and master the Unknown, everyone on the steamboat would believe him a fool.

Some day, after he had calculated everything worth knowing, he intended to explain his system in a book, so that everyone capable of working a simple problem in algebra could find the answers to the greatest problems confronting mankind. His book would turn the Unknown into the Known, and he never doubted that it would be one of the greatest books ever written.

But he realized that one should not set himself up as an authority until he is certain that he knows all the answers and, being a beginner, as yet he sometimes failed to get the correct answers. Nine out of ten, perhaps, but that still fell short of being sufficiently accurate for a dependable text that serious scholars might use with confidence.

When he produced an erroneous answer he was convinced that the fault lay, not in his system, but in his failure to get his facts straight at the outset.

The Hindus and the Arabs originated algebra, the Italians took a hand at it in the Middle Ages, and the British really developed it, but all their keenest mathematicians were merely mathematicians, accustomed to dealing with numbers and letters and symbols, so they all missed finding the most important factor until Barney carried their reasoning a step further, discovered the law of positivities and made use of it to open the door into the future, and perhaps even into the Hereafter.

His system is so simple that it is surprising that no one reasoned it out earlier. In place of symbols alone, he used them merely to represent such things as time and places and people, but mostly people. That is all there is to it.

Suppose one wishes to know if there is to be war. He starts with certain known factors, such as slave labor making tobacco and cotton profitable in the South, and the North caring nothing about raising cotton but centering its interest on factory goods, and he takes William Lloyd Garrison of the Anti-slavery Society fighting for the rights of the black man, and the Free Soil Party absorbing the Liberty Party and the Barnburners and even some Whigs and Democrats, and he measures them against John C. Calhoun, the fire-eating Carolina senator, and he takes many other known factors and persons and assigns each a symbol such as a, b, c or x, y, z, and then adds and subtracts and divides and takes the square root of this or that and carries something else to the nth power, and he comes up with an equation.

That is the system Barney utilized to prove to himself that there was to be a war, long before anyone else knew about it. He had worked it out as early as 1848 when he was twenty-four years old, but was unable to put his finger on the exact date because of the lack of certain happenings that should have been known factors.

He proved to himself not only that he was to get rich, but that he was to be free. Having worked out the war equation, he felt reasonably satisfied, for he reasoned that if he but waited long enough, the war would set him free.

But because of the missing factors the months dragged along and nothing happened; no war, that is. So he began to think more and more about running away. It would be considerably easier here than in Carolina or Georgia, for a station of the underground existed in almost every city of size along the Mississippi and Ohio. At St. Louis he met on two or three occasions with the local station agent, who worked out a promising plan for him.

Levi Coffin, known as the "president" of the Underground Railroad, lived across the Ohio from Louisville. Levi would be awaiting him on the Kentucky side of the river, and Barney was to slip away from the steamboat at night and meet him. Levi would row him across to the free soil side and would ship him, with other runaways, on the Underground from New Albany to Detroit and from there to Windsor, Ontario.

It was all planned out to the last detail and the nervous Barney was aflame with eagerness at the prospect of being a free man so soon.

He sat down and with his pencil worked out an algebraic equation which proved to him that he would soon be free, but then an unexpected development took the heart out of him. Big Thompson hired him out as second steward on a steamboat on the New

Orleans - St. Louis - Quincy run, ending his opportunity to get to Louisville.

Depressed in spirit, he sought out the St. Louis agent of the Underground, who revived his hopes with the assurance that Quincy offered even better facilities for escape. But the steamboat was heading south for New Orleans and more than a month would elapse before it reached Quincy on the return journey. He was planning and scheming every moment, but there were times when he was almost overwhelmed by doubt and uncertainty. So many things could go wrong!

If he tried and failed, almost certainly Big Thompson would sell him down the river as a cotton hand. At best he could expect a transfer to a southern run where he might never have another chance.

But it was now or never. Now in his middle twenties, he could not wait much longer, waiting for a war to free him.

He collected in his bundle everything he needed. He discarded his arithmetic, for the book would be of no help and an extra pair of shoes would be invaluable. He was aware that this branch of the Underground was routed for Canada by way of Chicago, but he could only guess the distance, whether it was wooded country, how many rivers or creeks he might be forced to swim or wade. He memorized his password and his instructions, repeating them by the hour so his memory might not trick him. Of course he dared set nothing down in writing.

His appetite fell off and at times anxiety left him physically ill. Although everything had been planned carefully, and the agent had informed him that almost everyone made it if they followed instructions to the letter and kept their mouths shut, still he could not fight back his doubts, even though he had worked out an equation and the answer came that he would surely make it this time.

He was far better prepared than most runaway slaves. He had saved nearly twenty dollars and owned a second pair of shoes. Most runaways lacked both shoes and money.

It was late afternoon when the steamboat swung in to the landing at Quincy, the paddle wheels backwatering and churning up foam, but raising less commotion than Barney's thumping heart.

There across the gangplank, only a few yards distant, lay free soil, but he dared not give it a second glance for fear someone might suspect what lay in his mind. He was trembling with eagerness and fear during the dragging, suspenseful hours he was forced to wait until darkness would aid his break. He feared that his nervous excitement might lead him to drop a tray or upset a table.

At first he had feared to take anyone into his confidence, even though convinced that none of the colored boys would let slip a word if they knew another to be planning to run away. Principally this was because they themselves might need help, but likewise because a betrayer stood an excellent chance of becoming a razor-slashed corpse floating in the river.

But at a free soil town like Quincy the white crew kept a close watch, since the steamboat company was legally responsible for hired-time hands. So escape was no matter of merely walking down the gangplank to freedom.

Finally Barney risked taking one of the bus boys into his confidence. Watching his chance, after dark he tossed his bundle over the side onto the landing and immediately stripped off his white jacket. This was the signal to his friend, who pushed a sack of grain over the off-shore rail.

It struck the water with a splash and the bus boy began to shout frantically, "Man overboard! Man overboard!" When everyone rushed to the off-shore rail Barney, heart pounding, unhurriedly strolled down the gangplank so that if he were seen, in the darkness he would be mistaken for a passenger.

Retrieving his bundle, he walked into the open door of a wharf warehouse and right on through to the far side of the building where a hack was drawn up alongside the loading platform. The white driver called out, "American House?" Barney answered by singing softly:

> And tell old Pharaoh
> To let my people go.

This was the recognition sign. The young driver said "Hop in," Barney hopped, and the hack moved away at an easy trot to avoid suspicion, but the clatter of hoofbeats through the deserted warehouse district left Barney quaking. The muscles of his thighs were aquiver, and at first he was unable to draw a breath and then he was panting like an exhausted hound.

He had been told that the first act of a runaway slave upon attaining freedom was to remove his shoes if he owned shoes, so his bare feet could touch free soil, but Barney had no time for such foolishness.

The way he had planned it, his friend was to keep shouting that it was Barney who had fallen overboard, so when they failed to drag him or his body from the water they would assume that he had drowned. This would account for his absence, so perhaps they would not notify the authorities to call out the bloodhounds.

Barney was wondering if the scheme was succeeding, but strangely he also was thinking of Big Thompson. He held no hate for his master, who had treated him humanely, but when he should have been thinking of himself he was wondering whether Big Thompson would be reimbursed for his missing slave.

Could they establish the fact that Barney had fallen overboard and drowned, that would be his owner's responsibility, but if he ran away, then the steamboat company would be held to account, although doubtless a lawsuit would be in order before his owner could recover the value of his human property.

The way he reasoned it out, even if the captain suspected that the hired-time hand had run away, he would try to make out that Barney had drowned, so the company would not be held liable for the twelve hundred dollars at which he was valued. Under these circumstances, the captain would refrain from notifying the authorities and Barney's chances would be vastly improved. He found himself wishing that his master would not lose out, but knowing Big Thompson, he was certain he would bring suit against the company in any event, and he could only hope he would win.

The hack clattered down the main street of Quincy, a strategic course, for who would dream of seeking a runaway there? Some time later it turned into the yard of a white frame cottage on the outskirts of the town and a mild little white man emerged to thrust his bald head in the hack to ask, "Who is it?"

Barney's voice was trembling as he responded, "A friend of a friend," the memorized password. He knew his questioner to be the agent or "conductor" of the Quincy underground station; a man who, in later years, was to become almost as famous as "President" Levi Coffin. Since he was a school teacher he was known as "the professor," but Barney never asked and never learned his real name.

The "professor" motioned him inside the cottage and questioned him briefly, mostly about the St. Louis agent. Having satisfied himself, he produced needle and thread and sewed a common black button in place of the third button on the runaway's shirt. He warned him not to let this button get torn off and not to change his shirt without changing the button, for it was his ticket and without it he could not be transported on the Underground. It was such a simple thing that no one would ever suspect its importance.

He warned Barney against talking to strangers and after inspecting his bundle and commenting on his prudence in bringing extra shoes to confuse the bloodhounds, he led him outside and across the alley to a stable in the rear of an undertaking establishment.

Here the teen-age hack driver, whom the fugitive slave took to be one of the "professor's" students, had unharnessed the team and harnessed it to a hearse. As directed, Barney climbed into the hearse and lay down in the coffin inside, too excited even to shudder. He marveled at the shrewd planning of the Underground operators, for who would suspect a hearse of containing living human contraband? Who would halt it in the middle of the night to search a coffin?

Barney's thoughts were racing as he lay jouncing about in the coffin as the hearse bore him away on the first leg of his long journey by underground. For easier breathing the coffin lid had been left askew, but even so he was close to stifling. Nevertheless he was fully prepared to slide the lid back in place if the hearse were halted; prepared, if need be, to suffocate rather than be dragged back into slavery.

He had been told that the greatest risk lay in the first leg of the journey by Underground, for here, close to the border of slave territory, bands of professional slave-hunters were active. They made use of bloodhounds, but what hound could trail a man in a hearse?

He knew well enough that unprepared plantation runaways stood little chance of eluding the bloodhounds, but the Underground was too expertly organized and operated to be outwitted by the slave-catchers.

Sixteen miles northeast of Quincy at 2 o'clock in the morning the hearse swung into a farmyard and drove right through the open door of a huge, red barn. A few years later this red barn came to be widely known as the first "waiting room" on the Quincy-Chicago division of the Underground. Barney gulped down deep breaths of fresh air as he clambered from the hearse. He resisted an impulse to drop to his knees and thank the young driver, for he remembered the "professor's" instruction to keep his mouth shut.

From the farmhouse emerged a chin-whiskered farmer the tail of his nightshirt stuffed within his overalls. After a moment of whispering with the driver, he lighted a lantern and made certain that Barney was wearing his black button.

"Climb up in the hay mow and get a good sleep, brother," he advised. "You'll stay there all day, and ma will bring you something to eat. Come nightfall, we'll move you on. Trust in the Lord and don't fret."

This was the first time a white man had ever called Barney "brother," and it was sweet to his ears. Before the farmer returned to the house he bowed his uncombed head and stood a moment with hands clasped in front of the bib of his overalls, praying. Barney bowed his head and prayed, too, and he never forgot that night as long as he lived.

But upon climbing the ladder and burrowing into the hay, he remained too excited and panicky to sleep. Occasionally he might doze off briefly, to wake with a start, imagining he could hear the distant baying of bloodhounds.

He kept thinking of Phoebe and how she had longed for her son to be free, and he surmised that if she knew of his escape she would rejoice and give thanks. He was resolving that, now that he had gained his freedom, he was going to show the world that he was the equal of his white half-brother.

Shortly after daylight the farmer's wife brought him a pan heaped with food, and a gourd filled with milk, and reminded him not to show his head until his friends came for him at nightfall.

He crawled back into the hay and this time slept soundly until late afternoon, when the housewife returned and fed him again. When darkness fell the farmer hitched up his team and directed Barney to lie in the wagon bed and piled cabbages over him and departed for the next station.

As far as Galesburg he was transported at night by agents of the Underground, usually by wagon. Thereafter the need for secrecy becoming less urgent, he would be given directions and would make his way afoot to the next station.

At Princeton a runaway named Albert had been held over, since two could get along better than one. He had no shoes, so Barney gave him his extra pair, and since he was penniless, gave him a dollar and Albert told him it was the most money he had ever owned and he wouldn't forget it.

The two remained together all the way to Chicago, plodding along all night every night, and no one stopped them or questioned them. At each station they would sleep in a barn and would be fed and given directions to the next stop, and until the last leg of the journey the only times they were not on their own was when an agent would hide them in a wagon and carry them across a river.

The last lap, from the suburbs on in, was made at night with a truck gardener taking a load of garden truck to market. He drew up at a tiny frame cottage in the Negro section, knocked at the door and asked, "You order two bales of black wool?"

The Chicago agent proved to be a little black man with a jutting frizzly black beard. He gave his name as Jack Jones, but Barney soon learned that this was merely his Underground name.

He housed them in the livery barn behind his cottage and told them it would be two or three days before the arrival of the next shipment, which they were to join until they finally reached Glory to God — the code name for Windsor, Ontario.

After his departure an attractive girl, half-white like Barney brought them corn bread and chittlings and coffee and warned them that they could not loaf in the barn while laying over, but would be expected to pay for their keep by helping Mister Wagoner with the horses.

When Barney asked, "Who's Mister Wagoner?" she put a hand

to her mouth as if she had let something slip, but after extracting a promise of secrecy, confided that H. O. Wagoner was the real name of the agent they knew as Jack Jones. Barney considered it strange that every other Underground agent had been white, but kept his reflections to himself.

In the morning Wagoner came to the barn and told them it was time to go to the restaurant for a bite. Barney thought he was joking, but no, the little black Underground agent reminded them that they were free men now and it was time they began acting accordingly.

He pointed out that of the twenty thousand persons living in Chicago, a sixth were colored, and that no one would suspect them to be fugitives if they only held their heads high and looked everyone straight in the eye, for there no longer was reason to hide or slink about through back alleys.

For the first time Barney experienced the exhilaration of freedom as he strode the streets in daylight, shoulders back and chest out, and no one gave him a second glance. It would have been no surprise had someone stepped right up and called him *Mister*.

Scrutinizing them thoughtfully, Wagoner pumped them judiciously, then informed Albert that he was to fork manure in the livery barn while Barney was to go out on the express wagon and help make deliveries since his manner of speech plainly indicated that he was educated.

Barney learned that Wagoner's father was a German and his mother a freed slave. Although a mulatto like Barney, his skin was much darker, almost black. He had been taught the alphabet by his father back at Hagerstown, Maryland, and had learned to write by using chalk on board fences. Learning mostly by copying store signs, he had found himself in trouble for copying *BEER 5¢* on the door of a church.

He did not tell that as a joke, and Barney was quick to grasp that he was wholly lacking in humor, but soon learned that the little black man possessed a fierce spirit that burned and flamed and scorched when it came to slavery and man's inhumanity to man. Barney surmised that he would make an eloquent, convincing camp meeting revival preacher, but he could not foresee what an impelling influence Wagoner was to exert on his own life.

He learned considerably more about this dedicated little black man that evening when the agent's attractive young kinswoman came home from her chambermaid job at a leading downtown hotel. After supper she pushed open the back screen door with her tiny foot and emerged to empty a pan of dishwater, and out by the pump Barney was washing his head merely by chance; or so it appeared.

She failed to repress a laugh at the spectacle he made, dripping wet, his blue-hazel eyes staring at her as if he were hypnotized, but her laughter was low and musical. No one ever possessed whiter, more even teeth.

She was tiny, not much more than shoulder-high to Barney. Her plump cheeks were somewhat lighter than his, matching the shade of blanched almonds, and her smiles brought forth tantalizing dimples. Her gentle and lovely brown eyes were so large that they made her oval face seem smaller.

She seldom laughed as she was laughing at him now, for her innate demureness of mien denied most young men more than a shy smile.

So concerned had he been with the acquisition of learning and with planning his escape from slavery, Barney had taken little interest in girls. But all at once as he took the dishpan from her hands he sensed something heretofore alien to his existence. It was new, strange, oddly disturbing yet wholly agreeable. His state of exaltation left him tongue-tied as he emptied the pan and rinsed it at the pump.

V

Julia A. Lyoni, sister of Wagoner's mulatto wife, was born on an Indiana farm August 15, 1827. When she entered Barney's life she was twenty-one years old and he was twenty-six.

As they sat together beside the pump and he found his voice and sought to learn more about her, Julia chose instead to talk about Wagoner, and while at the time he took little interest in the little Underground agent, he learned from her a great deal about him, some of which may be found in histories.

Born at Hagerstown February 27, 1816, Wagoner had spent most of his boyhood working as a field hand. He was a grown man before he attended school, but like Barney, had already taught himself to read and write.

After ten months in a Negro school at Cincinnati he was employed as a teacher in the same school. He cared little for teaching, and presently struck out for the West, reaching Galena, Illinois, where he learned to set type on the Northwestern *Gazette* and the Galena *Advertiser*.

Meanwhile he was burning with a desire to help his people, and in 1843 made his way to Chatham, Canada West, a haven for runaway slaves. He found a job setting type and writing editorials on the Chatham *Journal* and devoted his spare hours to teaching in a primary school for children of his own race.

The following year he married and presently, with his mulatto wife and their daughter, moved to Chicago and became compositor and editorial writer on the *Western Citizen*, an anti-slavery newspaper published by Z. Eastman. Eastman chanced to be a friend of a lanky young fellow just elected to Congress from Illinois on the Whig ticket; a man named Abraham Lincoln.

At that time virtually the only employment open to black men was common labor or the service trades. Wagoner was fortunate to be trained in a skilled trade, but was far from satisfied. He wanted a business of his own, and his limited capital was sufficient only to buy a horse and a rickety express wagon, so although he continued to work nights on the *Citizen,* by day he was in the express and livery business.

Two jobs were not enough for Wagoner. For several years he had been active in the operation of the Underground, and now his stable became the Chicago station of the system.

Sitting there in the back yard, Barney thought that he was pumping the lovely Julia about Wagoner and about herself, but before he realized it, she had wormed from him substantially the story of his life.

What was he planning to do when he reached Canada? Barney was forced to admit that he had given it little thought. He supposed a skilled cook could find work almost anywhere, and moreover he knew quite a bit about hogs and a little about panning gold.

She failed to enthuse at his prospects. He was too diffident to let her know about his law of positivities, was reluctant to disclose that its discoverer was destined to great accomplishment, although circumstances might compel him to take a cooking job temporarily.

And what name had he selected?

When a slave was manumitted, and later following emancipation, he frequently assumed the family name of his former owners. But not a runaway. Always a fugitive slave changed his name at once so he could not be traced. Now this was something Barney had given no thought.

While living on the Carolina plantation he dared not use the surname of his white father. If his name appeared on the plantation records, it was, "One buck nigger, age 10, name Barney," just as the records would list "One grey mule, age 16, name Barney," and that is the way his name would appear on the steamboat records, if such records were kept. The way most whites addressed him was, "Hey, boy," so actually he had needed no family name.

Now he was free to use his white father's surname, but it would be too easily traced. So he told Julia that he had not chosen a name, and did she have any suggestions?

At that time locomotives were named rather than numbered, and somewhere she had come across a steam engine named the Lancelot Ford and liked the sound of it. The last name seemed satisfactory to Barney, but he drew the line at Lancelot. As a compromise he agreed to use the initial only. So he came to be known as Barney L. Ford, and doubtless was the only man in history named for a locomotive.

Presently he took up with Wagoner a subject that had been weighing on his mind ever since his meeting with Julia. Now that he knew that a fugitive could remain undetected in Chicago, he was less than eager to proceed to Canada. Did Wagoner know where he might find a situation?

The agent conceded that it might be arranged, and suggested that he could use an educated man to help with the work of the Underground. If Barney cared to, he could work for his keep until something better turned up. So the following night, when Albert and the newly-arrived fugitives were loaded into the express wagon for the last lap of their journey to Glory to God, Barney remained behind.

Immediately he bought a good eight-dollar suit to replace the garments that had become so ragged on his flight from Quincy. To disguise himself he was growing a beard, but Julia detested it and made him shave it off, except for the mustache, which he wore all the rest of his life.

He was sleeping in Wagoner's barn, doing odd jobs to earn his keep, but after a week or two grew restless, for one can't marry without wages. Wagoner failed to find him a job as cook.

Julia brought word that the barber shop at the hotel where she was employed needed help, but Barney knew nothing of barbering. He spent two dollars for lessons, and so managed to get his first real job and to earn his first dollar as a free man.

He soon discovered that, as had been the case on the steamboat, his ability to quote the classics could bring more generous tips. Often he received as much as twenty-five cents from a dumfounded customer.

Meanwhile he was helping Wagoner with his Underground duties. At intervals of ten days to a month shipments of from two to five fugitive slaves passed through the Chicago station on their way to Canada.

Virtually all the "freight" they forwarded originated in Illinois and Missouri. Most of these runaways were above the intelligence level of the ordinary plantation hand, for nearly always it was the ones with the most enterprise and initiative that made the break for freedom.

Now it was Barney rather than Wagoner who delivered the fugitives. He realized that he was taking a chance on a jail sentence. The risk troubled him less than the possibility of being identified and returned to slavery.

Wagoner was continually writing letters begging funds to maintain the operations of the Underground. Most of the money came from anti-slavery societies at Boston, Albany, Philadelphia, and Washington, D. C.

Under his code name of Jack Jones he kept in close touch with the leaders of the Massachusetts and Pennsylvania anti-slavery organizations and with individual Abolitionists in the northern states.

Once he permitted Barney to read a letter from a young Boston lawyer named Charles Sumner, who had fought the annexation of Texas as a slave state. In 1848 Sumner was supporting Martin Van Buren in his unsuccessful campaign to return to the White House as candidate of the Free Soil Party.

Another letter came from Frederick Douglass, the runaway slave who had become such a compelling orator and anti-slavery leader.

All this time, when he was not delivering Underground shipments or taking Julia for Sunday excursions in the express wagon, Barney was spending his evenings studying. No longer was he reading haphazardly or for pleasure alone. Wagoner kept lending him books and tracts on economics and sociology and politics. The Underground agent lacked his acquaintance with history and the classics, but had done an immense amount of reading and writing on subjects of direct interest to him.

From time to time Barney kept up with his study of algebra, which to Wagoner appeared an utter waste of time. Barney never disclosed to him or to Julia the secret of his law of positivities for fear they might think him a simpleton, but he had proved to his own satisfaction that his system was reliable and accurate. Hadn't it told him he was to be free?

He had never forgot the words of his mother, "Some day you stand on gallery like young master, white folks call you *Mister*." Now that Julia had come into his life he was eagerly ambitious to make that prediction come true. His discovery of the law of positivities, he was confident, destined him to great accomplishment.

The baffled Phoebe had cried, "Mama try to he'p you, but she don't know how!" Now Barney was learning how to help himself. But even though he was free and earning wages he was far from satisfied. He was dreaming of the day when he would own and operate a barber shop of his own.

All this time he had been sleeping in the livery barn, but in 1849, a year following his escape from slavery, when he was twenty-seven, he and Julia were married and he moved in with the Wagoners.

He liked barbering because it brought him in constant contact with men of quality. He enjoyed listening to the discussions of business and politics, and constantly studied and imitated the speech of his leading customers.

With all of Wagoner's reading and editorial writing, his speech was still tinged with his old plantation accent, and it failed to make for respect on the part of the whites. So far as Barney was concerned, he was certain that the whites would never call him *Mister* until he had perfected his speech.

Preparing to start his own barber shop, he persuaded Wagoner to teach him a simple system of bookkeeping, which was less interesting but more practical than his studies in higher mathematics. Julia still kept her chambermaid job, and they were saving to start his shop, and it might have materialized had Barney not suffered a relapse of the gold fever.

The newspapers were blazoning the news of the discovery of gold in California. The barber shop customers ceased to discuss politics and even the prize fights. Gold was all that held their interest. Gold! Why, it was there merely for the trouble of washing it from the sandbars! Fortunes were being made overnight. A man was crazy to stick with banking or the stock market when he could go out there and get rich quick!

Everyone was working out some means to quit his job or sell his business to follow the example of the Argonauts who were sailing 'round the Horn, or crossing to the Pacific by way of Panama or Nicaragua. Listening to all their wishful talk, it is little wonder that Barney succumbed.

Why should he remain tied down to a barber job when he might get rich in the gold fields? The prospects of owning his own shop were beginning to appear sadly uninviting alongside his fever dreams.

At least, from his experience in the gold fields of Georgia, he knew something about operating a Long Tom, which was considerably more than most of these fast talkers knew.

At first Julia was opposed to his plan to join the gold rush. No one got rich at barbering, but at least it was a living. Besides, where would they get the money to go to California?

Barney kept it a secret from her, but he had gone back to his law of positivities to learn if he were really to get rich. The answer came out, certainly he was to get rich, but he was ashamed to tell Julia for fear she would make fun of him and of his system, but he continued to argue with her.

By the following year a good share of his customers had departed to swell the ranks of the Forty-niners. The gold fever was sweeping the country like the cholera. Tales of sudden riches filtered back and spread like a prairie fire.

The headlines told how Commodore Cornelius Vanderbilt was master-minding a group of capitalists who had won a concession from the Republic of Nicaragua to build a huge ship canal. Pending the start of actual building on the Nicaraguan canal they had arranged to transport the thousands of gold seekers up the San Juan River to Lake Nicaragua and then by stagecoach across the mountains to the Pacific, to complete the trip by steamship. It was shorter and faster than the trip 'round the Horn, and cheaper than the Panama crossing.

So far as Barney was concerned, the journey was far beyond his means. The Panama crossing came to $600; by Vanderbilt's

Nicaragua route, to $400. He was heartbroken to think of being forced to abandon this wonderful opportunity to get rich in the mines.

But by 1850 the flood of emigration and the competition between the Panama and Nicaragua lines had brought the first-class fare down to $150 and steerage passage to $45, and this he could afford. He kept arguing with Julia, but for long she remained adamant.

One persuasive argument Barney used on her was the recent admission of California as a free state. When it came to panning gold, there was no color line. And well she knew that no colored man could hope to get rich operating a Chicago barber shop.

What was she afraid of, anyway? He not only knew how to pan gold, but could barber and cook, so even if he failed to strike it rich he could always earn a good living.

And he was educated, wasn't he? Of his race, not one in ten thousand could boast his book learning. Physically he was capable of standing hardships. Did she want to stand in the way of his getting rich so some day they could welcome guests on the gallery of their own gold-bought mansion?

In the course of time his constant pressure wore her down and she agreed that if it was what he wanted, she was prepared to go, and when would they start?

Barney had planned to go by himself and then send for her after he struck it rich, but she wouldn't listen to such a plan. She had worked hard all her life and was well and strong. She was a capable chambermaid, and if need be could find a job in a San Francisco or Sacramento hotel. In the end she had her way.

The cheapest way to start on the Nicaragua crossing was to go down the Mississippi and take one of the Vanderbilt Line steamships from New Orleans, but Barney dared not risk a journey through slave territory, down the very river where he was known to so many.

So July of 1851 found Barney and Julia steerage passengers on the 1500-ton Vanderbilt Line side-wheeler, the *Prometheus*, en route from New York to Greytown, Nicaragua.

VI

In 1851 Greytown was little more than a collection of palm-thatch huts on stilts at the edge of the steaming jungle where the San Juan River empties into the Caribbean. It was important solely because it was supposed to become the eastern terminus of the Nicaraguan Canal that Vanderbilt and his moneyed friends proposed to build.

The discovery of gold at Sutter's Mill in California in 1848 had touched off a world-wide chain reaction. First, Vanderbilt and his friends had maneuvered the concession from the Nicaraguan government, such as it was, to build a canal linking the Atlantic and Pacific.

Already small boats could ascend the San Juan River to Lake Nicaragua to within twelve miles of the Pacific, and except for some dredging in the river and several locks to by-pass rapids, apparently all that remained to be done was to cut the canal through those twelve miles on the west side.

But the British had no intention of standing by idly while the Americans built a canal that would rival Suez and link the Atlantic with the Pacific. It would control the western seas in time of war and would be of immense importance commercially.

They had claimed a protectorate over Honduras on the Caribbean coast, but its southern boundary had never been determined. They claimed that it extended along the Mosquito Coast as far south as the San Juan River, where the little palm-shack port at the river mouth was known as San Juan del Norte. Without notice to the United States a British landing force took over the little town and changed its name to Greytown.

With the port in their possession the British would control the eastern entrance of the proposed canal and could collect port fees on all its traffic and in time of war could close the canal to their enemies.

Since there was no proof as to the exact southern boundary of Honduras, there was little the United States government could do about it.

This was the situation in July of 1851 when Barney and Julia disembarked from the *Prometheus,* assuming Greytown to be merely a stopover on their way to California. They discovered that they must lay over for three days until the river steamboat descended the San Juan from Lake Nicaragua.

The only place to stay was a palm-thatch frame hotel operated by a plump German woman who charged two dollars a night for a hammock or for a pallet on the floor.

As far south as Greytown the steaming Mosquito Coast was probably the most unhealthy region in the western hemisphere. For fear of malaria, cholera and yellow fever none but the natives dared drink anything but boiled water. Before the arrival of the river steamboat Barney was taken down with a raging fever.

For fear of contagion Barney and his wife were refused passage on the steamboat and the German woman ejected them from her hotel. Their dilemma was serious, for there was no doctor in Greytown and they were forced to rely on the physicians of the ocean steamships.

Julia rented a palm-thatch native shack on the edge of the jungle, bought hammocks and forced him to chew cinchona bark, the remedy of the natives for almost every ailment. Although she, too, stood a chance of becoming ill, she nursed him through his long illness. Her task was the more difficult since she spoke no Spanish, and few aside from the British officials spoke English.

The corporation set up by Commodore Vanderbilt to build the canal was known as the Accessory Transit Company, and its warehouses lay across the bay from Greytown on a spit of sand called Punta Arenas. Nearly all the American company employees lived there; mostly working the river steamboats. A clause of the concession from the Nicaraguan government permitted the company to operate a steamboat-stagecoach line along the route pending completion of the canal.

In spite of all that the steamship medicos could do for him, Barney remained a desperately sick man for many weeks. Lying beneath his mosquito bar during his convalescence, listening to the squalling of the parakeets in the palm and ceiba jungle, he found ample time to think.

The plump German hotel proprietress was clearing a huge profit renting hammocks and providing indifferent meals for the gold-seekers at almost any price she chose to charge. Her place was always filled, and Barney kept telling Julia that a hotel serving first-class American meals at fair prices should prove a money-making venture.

The German woman served almost as many go-backers as gold-seekers. A go-backer was a disappointed gold-seeker who had lost everything in the California diggings and was going back home. As Barney became strong enough to move about once more, he found that the luckless fellows had had their fill of California. For each person that struck it rich, they reported, a hundred lost all they owned, and the fortunate ones were the ones with enough money for the fare to return home.

Barney was losing his enthusiasm for California and came to the conclusion that he would be wiser to go into the hotel business right here at Greytown. As he reasoned it out, when the canal was completed, the port was destined to become a great city, perhaps the size of Chicago, and anyone shrewd enough to get in on the ground floor was certain to do well. He was a skilled cook and Julia was an experienced chambermaid, and there was every reason to suppose that they could operate a hotel better than the German woman.

To test his judgment he worked out another algebraic equation, and it confirmed his belief. He talked it over with Julia, and she agreed with him.

His actual decision, however, was based on another factor. Back in his steamboating days on the Chattahoochee he had dreamed of migrating to the Negro republic of Liberia, where all men were equal and the color of one's skin was no drawback. To his surprise, here in Greytown he found precisely the conditions he had heard existed in Liberia.

Long ago, two slave ships from Africa had been wrecked on the Mosquito Coast and the black men had mingled with the natives and now most of the population had more or less Negro blood. They were known as Zambos to distinguish them from the Black Caribs, descendants of Negro slaves from the Caribbean islands.

There remained little pure native stock, and aside from some Spanish traders, the only whites were the comparatively few British officials and the American employees of the Transit Company, but there was a sprinkling of *mestizos* of mixed Spanish and Indian blood.

With all this mixture of races, a color line was unknown. This was the condition Barney had dreamed of finding in Liberia. Here the color of one's skin made not the slightest difference.

So Barney and Julia abandoned their California plans, began looking about and found a good-size frame building that they could buy on time payments. Hammocks and tableware cost but little, but by the time Barney had the sign painted and nailed up in front, all their savings were gone. The sign read: *United States Hotel. B. L. Ford, Prop.*, and Julia was immensely proud to have her husband's name where everyone could see it. He would not admit that he felt the same way, but was delighted to be in business for himself and working for wages no longer.

Their clean accommodations and tasty meals speedily brought them all the guests they could care for. All the Americans stopped at Ford's place, even the American ambassador and Commodore Vanderbilt himself when traveling back and forth. All praised Barney's cooking.

Ford's United States Hotel was the regular eating place of Joseph F. Fabens, the lean American commercial agent, for Joseph N. Scott, the whiskered agent of the Transit Company, and for almost every traveler of consequence.

Fabens called Barney the American mayor, and he was not far from the truth, for the hotelman was held in high regard by all his countrymen. He had virtually eliminated his plantation accent, and his speech was so precise that it was taken for granted that he was a college graduate.

Among his regular luncheon guests was the florid British acting vice-consul, James Geddes, distinguished by bushy red Dundreary whiskers. Once Barney chanced to mention that Horatio Nelson, then a young officer in the British navy, had lost an eye in 1780 while leading an assault on Castillo Viejo, the Spanish fortress guarding the lake source of the San Juan, and the vice-consul was so astonished that he almost lost his monocle.

He asked Barney if he were a Harvard man, and when the hotel keeper soberly replied that he had acquired his Ph.D. in the School of Experience, the British looked thoughtful and, unwilling to admit that he had never heard of this great Yankee institution of higher learning, merely exclaimed, "My word!"

Influential and prosperous, Barney was becoming highly respected throughout Greytown. The hotel was thriving and he was looking forward to the time when the port would become a great city and he would be a millionaire.

No one could surpass tough old Commodore Vanderbilt when it came to explosive profanity, and on his visits to Greytown he spent most of his time quarreling with the British authorities over the payment of port dues.

Punta Arenas was mostly sandy beach, too shallow for his oceangoing steamships, which were compelled to use the embarcadero in Greytown harbor. But when the puppet port authorities set up by the British sought to collect port dues, he informed them profanely that even if the United States of America recognized Great Britain's claim to the territory, he sure as hell didn't, and for all he cared, Queen Victoria could go take a running jump into the Thames.

In consequence the puppet port officials raided his warehouses at Punta Arenas and seized merchandise sufficient to satisfy their claims and perhaps a bit more for personal contingencies. The commodore was compelled to appeal to the State Department at Washington.

To cap the climax, in June of 1854 the river steamboat *Routh* collided with a native *bongo* and the captain, T. T. Smith, whipped out his pistol and killed the pilot of the native craft. United States

Minister Solon Borland chanced to be a passenger on the steamboat.

When the *Routh* reached the embarcadero the port authorities attempted to place the captain under arrest, but Borland thwarted them by hiding him at the American consulate. From the veranda of his hotel Barney watched a mob cluster about the consulate, loudly demanding the Yankee skipper.

Borland stepped out to explain that since the shooting occurred up-river, outside the town, the Greytown authorities lacked jurisdiction. Someone in the mob threw a broken beer bottle at him, and it cut his face.

So he, too, protested to the State Department. Would Uncle Sam permit his official representative to be insulted with a beer bottle?

The authorities in Washington were seeking an excuse to oust the British and regain control of the eastern terminus of the proposed canal. Doubtless their unaccustomed boldness was due to the fact that the bulk of the British navy was engaged in fighting the Crimean War. So Secretary of State W. L. Marcy dispatched the sloop-of-war *Cyane,* under Captain George H. Hollins, to Greytown with an ultimatum.

Barney could see Her Majesty's schooner, the *Bermuda,* riding at anchor in the harbor the night of July 11 when the *Cyane* steamed in and most of Greytown's puppet officials sought safety in the jungle.

Captain Hollins landed with a squad of Marines and called a meeting at Barney's hotel. Attending were Fabens, the American commercial agent; Geddes, British vice-consul; Scott, the Transit Company agent; Diezman, captain of the port; and A. Siguad, the French mulatto puppet mayor.

Captain Hollins demanded within twenty-four hours an official apology from Her Britannic Majesty for insulting the United States with a beer bottle; plus twenty-four thousand dollars cash indemnity for seizing Commodore Vanderbilt's property.

The British vice-consul loftily rejected his demands, intimating that HMS *Bermuda* would blow him right out of the water. Captain Hollins shrugged and posted a notice on the embarcadero announcing that he would begin shelling the town at daylight. He instructed Fabens to move all Americans across the harbor to Punta Arenas, and the commercial agent delegated the task to Barney.

Commander Jolly of HMS *Bermuda*, too proud to attend the meeting, sent word that he was prepared to protect the interests of his government. In reply the cocky Hollins sent him a copy of the proclamation.

Barney and Julia were sick at heart as they took their cash from the till, packed their belongings in a trunk, and prepared to abandon the hotel. Loyal Americans, they saw no reason why their property should be destroyed merely because Washington wished to curb British aggression.

Seated on their trunk in the shade of the warehouse at Punta Arenas the following morning, they watched the *Cyane* open fire on Greytown with its big guns. Commander Jolly meekly withdrew HMS *Bermuda* from the harbor as the American vessel shelled the town.

Among the first buildings to be destroyed was Barney's United States Hotel, but he strove to hide his heartbreak as he patted Julia's shoulder and sought to still her sobbing.

All day the *Cyane* shelled the town. One Marine with a torch could have accomplished the same results more quickly, effectively, and cheaply, but such a course would not have been in keeping with the best navy shot-and-shell tradition and could not be expected to produce such big headlines in the American newspapers.

So despite all their efforts and hard work, Barney and Julia were beached, with only their trunk filled with personal belongings and a few hundred dollars from the cash drawer. It was a crushing blow, but before nightfall Barney had found a job.

No steamboat could pass the Castillo Rapids on the river, so the *San Carlos* carried passengers as far as the rapids and transferred them to the *La Virgen*, which took them on to Virgin Bay on Lake Nicaragua. Barney was hired as steward on the *La Virgen*.

"Mister Ford" no longer, now he was addressed as "Barney" or merely "boy." It was an abrupt comedown for one who had become a leader in the community, recognized as the "American mayor," but he swallowed his humiliation, saved his wages, and eight months later bought the California Hotel at Virgin Bay and established himself in business once more.

The bombardment of Greytown might have resulted in war, had Great Britain's forces not been engaged in the Crimea.

The buildings at Virgin Bay, unlike the palm-thatch shacks at Greytown, were of stone or adobe, and the climate was immeasurably more healthful.

Barney had paid scant heed to the politics of Nicaragua, which seemed embroiled in a perpetual state of revolution. The Legitimists — known as *calzados,* or aristocrats, because they wore shoes — recently had ejected the Democrats, and two months after Barney bought his new Hotel William Walker landed his filibuster expedition from California with the announced intention of aiding the ousted Democrats.

Barney favored Walker, since he appeared to be on the side of the underdog, but paid little attention to his campaign until the night of July 6, when the invaders fought their way from the west coast up the macadamized Transit Company highway to the town of Rivas, only three miles from Virgin Bay. When they heard the shooting, Barney and Julia barricaded the hotel doors, but for the time being, the filibuster expedition by-passed Virgin Bay.

On the morning of September 8 Barney awoke to find the streets swarming with the American adventurers and their native allies. Uneasily he watched them build their campfires and prepare their morning meal in the shade of the buildings and then spread their blankets to sleep after their night march.

Most of the Americans came from the California gold fields; tall, sun-tanned and bearded, wearing heavy wool breeches, miners' boots, felt hats, and flannel shirts of blue, grey or red. Their native allies wore white cotton shirts and knee-length cotton trousers. A red ribbon tied to a shirt button constituted the only uniform of these Democrats.

Although the American newspapers called them The Immortals, Barney thought they looked like tramps, and Walker himself, except for his cold, grey eyes, was unimpressive in appearance. With members of his staff he rode into Virgin Bay later in the morning, came to the hotel, and politely asked if Barney could serve the group meals. They got what he requested, and Barney prudently presented no bill.

Walker seldom smiled, never raised his voice. His expressionless face reminded Barney of the Mississippi river gamblers.

While the party was being served, a breathless courier rushed in with word that the forces of General Santos Guardiola, the Legitimist leader known as The Butcher, were approaching from the north. As unperturbed as if he were choosing dessert, Walker ordered a company deployed north along the picket fences and irrigating ditches, another to occupy the residence section on the hillside behind the town, and a third to serve as rear guard on the Transit highway.

Julia's expression revealed her alarm, so the filibuster leader quietly suggested to Barney that he take her to the Transit Company brick warehouse, which was surrounded by a high wooden stockade.

Barney never forgot that day. The Legitimists came charging into town, the barefoot soldiers in cotton knee pants, their officers in gold-braid black coats. The American sharpshooters decimated the front ranks and the attack wavered and broke, despite the sword-whipping administered by the officers.

Meanwhile, pistol in hand, Walker was making the rounds of his front positions, paying no more heed to the whistling bullets than if they had been mosquitoes. Shortly the re-formed Legitimists charged again, and this time all of Walker's men except the rear guard fell back to the warehouse stockade, where Barney and Julia were crouching, hoping that the hotel would remain undamaged.

When the attackers reached a point within forty feet of the stockade, Walker raised his pistol and began to shoot. This was the signal for his *Norte Americanos* to surge through the gates with fixed bayonets, and again Guardiola's disorganized forces fell back.

Late in the afternoon the Legitimists launched a third unsuccessful attack and withdrew for the night, with sixty killed as against the defenders' two. Walker himself had stopped two spent bullets.

During the night the Democrats abandoned the town, taking

with them all the liquor in Barney's hotel. Within a few weeks President Castellon died of cholera and the Legitimists were ready to admit defeat. Walker took over and set up a puppet president, Patricio Rivas.

Barney soon learned that the Walker filibuster expedition was linked with United States politics and the Wall Street struggle between Commodore Vanderbilt and his business foes.

While Vanderbilt was traveling in Europe, Charles Morgan of the Morgan steamship lines, and Cornelius K. Garrison, gained control of the Transit Company in a Wall Street coup. They paid Walker $20,000 to refrain from molesting the company property and guaranteed him free transportation on their ships for his recruits and supplies.

In the United States talk of secession was spreading. Barney began to hear whispers that Walker, a Southerner, was plotting to set up a Republic of Central America intended to become an ally of the slave states in case of war. More disturbing were dark hints that he favored slavery for Nicaragua.

Refusing to admit defeat, Vanderbilt maneuvered about until he regained control of the Transit Company. Morgan and Garrison promptly induced Walker to seize the company property.

With the Walker regime opposed to him, Vanderbilt persuaded Costa Rica to declare war on Nicaragua and financed an army of Costa Rican invaders, who speedily captured Virgin Bay. Walker was bedridden with the dengue fever and was unable to lead his troops, which were soundly defeated.

Both armies neglected to bury their dead, and the resultant cholera epidemic killed more soldiers on both sides than had been killed in battle, as well as countless civilians.

The remnant of the Costa Rican army withdrew from Nicaragua. Walker deposed his puppet president and assumed the office himself. One of his first decrees abolished all acts of the Confederated Congress of Central America.

This confederation had abolished slavery, and although it had separated into individual republics, up to this time its fundamental laws had remained unquestioned. The principal effect of Walker's decree was the restoration of slavery in Nicaragua.

To Barney and Julia, the shock was worse even than the destruction of their property in the Greytown bombardment. After discussing the situation, they concluded that Nicaragua was no place for anyone with Negro blood.

In Vanderbilt, Walker had more than met his match. The Costa Rican army had given up the fight, but the commodore was more powerful than the army. Even though Walker had seized the river steamboats and the Transit Company warehouses and stagecoaches, Vanderbilt held the winning card, for he still controlled the ocean steamship lines on both the Atlantic and Pacific, over which must be transported supplies and recruits. Before Walker realized his helplessness, the commodore was strangling the life out of his dictatorship. He finally surrendered to the United States navy, only to organize another unsuccessful filibuster expedition in Central America. He came to his end before the rifles of a firing squad in Honduras.

The Crimean War came to an end in 1856, but by that time it was apparent that in all probability the Nicaraguan Canal never would be built, so the British withdrew from Greytown, but never paid the twenty-four-thousand-dollar indemnity and never apologized for the beer bottle insult.

Everyone was satisfied except Barney and the other Americans whose property had been destroyed in the bombardment. Later they filed a memorial to Congress asking reimbursement of their losses, but it never emerged from committee.

Following the British abandonment of Greytown, the Nicaraguans restored the town's original name of San Juan del Norte. In course of time sand filled the harbor, precluding its use by ocean steamships.

As for Virgin Bay on Lake Nicaragua, the volcano Ometepec buried the town in cinders and within a few years the jungle engulfed the ruins. Actually the reason that the Nicaraguan Canal was not built in place of the Panama Canal is because of the hazard of the volcanoes.

But all this happened after Barney sold the California Hotel and returned home. It had been but a few years since he had escaped from slavery, but when he and Julia reached Chicago, they had accumulated a cash profit of $4,940 from their hotel ventures in Nicaragua.

This was no surprise to Barney, since he had worked it out by means of his law of positivities, and from the outset had known he was destined to become rich.

VII

H. O. Wagoner was delighted at Barney's return, for the little black man's various interests were becoming burdensome and he was feeling the need of a trustworthy aide. He was still writing blazing editorials for the *Citizen*, still operated his livery business largely as a blind for the Underground, but recently had invested his savings of $7,000 in a flour mill adjoining the livery stable. Also, he now had six children.

Barney had been considering his original plan to establish a barber shop, but Wagoner offered to sell him the livery business at a bargain if he would take over operation of the Underground station.

In Nicaragua Barney not only had prospered in the hotel business, but had been accepted on a basis of equality and had been recognized as a leader in the community. Had he cared to, he might have boasted of accomplishing more within a few years than any other runaway slave.

Still he was far from satisfied, and kept thinking of another runaway slave, Frederick Douglass, who had not become rich but who was accomplishing much for his people.

Barney was a bit ashamed because during his years in Nicaragua he had been working only for his own selfish interests and had done nothing to help the members of his race. He told himself that his mother would not be pleased, if she knew.

He was confident that he could do better for himself operating a barber shop than running a livery business, but now he considered himself well-to-do and was in little need of more money. He took up Wagoner's offer so he could emulate Douglass and help his people.

The Fugitive Slave Law adopted in 1850 provided a one-thousand-dollar fine or six months in jail for aiding a slave to escape, so Barney was well aware that he was taking a chance of winding up behind bars.

Congress had approved the Missouri Compromise years earlier. Except in Missouri, it prohibited slavery north of Latitude 36°30'.

Up to this time the slave states had controlled Congress, but the states north of the Mason and Dixon line were settling up so rapidly that they were gaining votes steadily in the House. To gain more slave state votes in Congress, Texas was annexed, and the Southern fire-eaters supported war with Mexico in the belief that California would side with the South.

The Fugitive Slave Act was designed to aid the slave owners to recover their runaways, but it proved to be largely ineffective. Enforcement was left up to special commissions, and local law enforcement officers no longer were held responsible for capturing fugitive slaves.

So when Barney took over operation of the Chicago station of the Underground, he found conditions considerably easier. Many persons, including local police officers and sheriff's deputies, were aware of what he was doing, but felt that now enforcement was the responsibility of the special commissions only. Among the officers who actively aided him was City Detective Allan Pinkerton, who later founded the Pinkerton private detective agency.

Considerable hazards still remained. The population of Chicago was far from being unanimously opposed to slavery. Many Southern Democrats were complaining violently because the Fugitive Slave Law was not being enforced, and were doing everything in their power to aid the enforcement officers.

Barney took over not only the actual operation of the station, receiving and forwarding the "freight," but also most of Wagoner's correspondence with the leaders of the anti-slavery cause.

The young Boston lawyer, Charles Sumner, had been elected United States Senator from Massachusetts by a union of Free Soilers and Democrats. Barney failed to meet him face to face until some years later when he was lobbying in Washington, but his mail acquaintance with the leader of the anti-slavery cause was to prove immensely helpful to him in later years when Barney himself was active in politics. Although he did not realize it at the time, another who was to help him later was Editor Eastman of the *Citizen,* friend of that lanky young Illinois lawyer, Abraham Lincoln.

It was a red-letter day for Barney when the orator and organizer about whom he had read so much in the *Liberator* called at the Chicago station of the Underground. Mulatto Frederick Douglass, a few years older than Barney, had escaped from slavery at Baltimore in 1838. A born orator, presently he was touring the country raising funds for the Underground.

Douglass told Barney that during a visit to England a group of Quakers, fearing that he might be kidnapped back into slavery, raised $750 to buy his freedom. This gave Barney an idea.

He was willing to risk jail, but lived in constant dread of being identified and returned to slavery. But now he wondered, why could not he, too, buy his freedom? Prospering, he could well afford it.

So through his Underground connections he set about to locate Big Thompson and offer $500 for his manumission. No one could find his last master, and Barney supposed that he had succumbed either to the rheumatism or whisky.

Years earlier the fire-eating Carolinian, Calhoun, had failed in an effort on behalf of a law to permit slave owners to transport their human property into free states. But in 1854 during the debate on the Kansas-Nebraska bill, Senator Stephen A. Douglas came up with essentially the same Calhoun proposal, and to the astonishment of all but a few, his bill was approved.

In effect it scuttled the Missouri Compromise and to all intents and purposes, legalized slavery everywhere in the United States, for it was necessary only to buy slaves in the South before removing them to the North, to remain within the law.

Although this was a blow to Barney, there was little he could do about it. In 1857 the Dred Scott decision seemed to him to open the entire country to the slave owners.

For some months Barney received no mail from Senator Sumner, who was recuperating from injuries incurred when the slave-state Congressman, Preston Brooks, attacked him with a cane in the Senate chamber. Although three years elapsed before he could resume his Senate seat, Sumner still was a political leader of abundant influence, and at length began to answer Barney's letters and to aid him in the work of the Underground.

On the night of June 22, 1857, Barney and Julia called at Wagoner's cottage, and the little black man with the jutting beard herded the womenfolk and children into the kitchen and led Barney into the back parlor where the lamp was turned down and introduced him to a white visitor he addressed as Nelson Hawkins. Barney never forgot him, a man in his middle fifties, although his grey beard and his stoop made him appear older; never forgot his eaglebeak nose and grey-blue eyes that seemed to spark fire when he was aroused. They were discussing the situation in bleeding Kansas, which upon passage of the Kansas-Nebraska bill, had become a battleground for the free soil and slave forces. The visitor was reticent in the presence of Barney, who soon made an excuse to depart.

The following day Wagoner disclosed that Nelson Hawkins actually was the famous Free Soil agitator, John Brown or, as the newspapers called him, Ossawatomie Brown.

The next night four fugitive slaves were brought to the livery barn by Detective Pinkerton, and Barney recalled reading newspaper reports of a raid into Missouri in which Brown and his followers had liberated them.

Only occasionally thereafter did Barney lay eyes on Ossawatomie. He appeared in Chicago again on April 25, 1858, but as he was being shadowed, did not visit the station. Instead he registered under his own name at the Adams House and gave out savagely unrestrained interviews to the newsmen.

Two months later, on June 22, he appeared unexpectedly at the station late at night, using the name Shubel Morgan. Barney took part in this meeting, but merely as an onlooker.

Actually, there was but little opportunity to talk in the presence of John Brown, but his every word compelled attention. He reminded Barney of an Old Testament prophet.

The traffic handled by the Underground was growing steadily, largely because of the Kansas-Missouri trouble, which John Brown took pains to keep stirred up. Every few days the newspapers carried reports of clashes between the Kansas Free Soilers and the Missouri "border ruffians."

Early in 1859 Brown led the highly-publicized raid into Missouri during which his band killed five whites and liberated eleven slaves. In ensuing weeks newspaper headlines kept reporting the progress of the party by Underground across Kansas, Nebraska, Iowa and Illinois on their flight to Canada.

To those in the North it was regarded as a triumph of justice and virtue, but editors below the Mason and Dixon line branded it a high-handed violation of constitutional rights and safeguards.

Many persons were led to wonder how, with all this newspaper publicity, it was possible to transport such a large group across four states without discovery by the enforcement officers. As a matter of fact, hundreds of persons, including reporters for the Northern newspapers, knew where they spent almost every night, but maintained a self-imposed conspiracy of silence.

Meanwhile, still using the name Shubel Morgan, Brown had gone on ahead to Detroit to meet Frederick Douglass, and the two were waiting to ferry the fugitives across to Canada. They had sent word to Wagoner and Barney to prepare to care for eleven bales of wool in their livery barn.

Barney was vastly disturbed by the newspaper publicity. Up to this time all his Underground work had been carried on in an atmosphere of the deepest secrecy.

This time Allan Pinkerton himself met the fugitive party at West Liberty to make certain that no reward-seeking local officer became too inquisitive. Loading them in a boxcar, he remained with them until they reached the Chicago railroad yards. Wagoner and Barney met the party with two livery rigs and brought them to the livery barn under cover of darkness.

Advised to prepare for eleven, Barney was dismayed to find twelve, an infant having been born in the boxcar. The party included two men, three women and seven children, counting the baby, which had no regard for secrecy and alarmed Barney with its bawling.

This was the largest shipment ever handled by the station and since the barn was too small, some were hidden in the adjoining mill, and Julia and her sister took the mother and baby into the Wagoner home with the six Wagoner children.

Barney had planned to keep them only overnight, but to his dismay Pinkerton informed him that it would be several days before the shipment could be forwarded to Detroit.

Meanwhile the newspapers were reporting that the party had by-passed Chicago and was being smuggled toward Canada in wagons, but this was merely a device to avert suspicion. On the third night Pinkerton gave the word, and Barney and Wagoner drove the fugitives to the freight yards and loaded them into a Michigan Central boxcar, and Barney heaved a sigh of relief when he got rid of the baby.

John Brown and Douglass were waiting at Detroit, and Brown called in the newsmen and boasted that this was but the beginning. Although few were aware of it, already he was planning his Harper's Ferry raid. Most of the freed slaves settled at Chatham, Ontario.

Historians wrote that this affair in which Barney participated was "the boldest exploit of the Underground Railroad."

Barney had ample reason to be disturbed at the publicity accorded the affair. Within a week Wagoner's flour mill was burned to the ground. None could prove that the slavery sympathizers were responsible, but Barney and Wagoner needed no proof. For some time thereafter Barney slept in the livery barn to guard against prowlers.

The loss of the flour mill was a blow to Wagoner, for he carried no fire insurance. It failed to deter him from continuing to accept the risks of the Underground operations, for the little black man possessed an indomitable spirit, and he set about rebuilding the mill, mortgaging his home to raise the money.

Barney never laid eyes on John Brown again. The following October the determined old zealot set the country ablaze with his audacious raid on Harper's Ferry. Barney was miserable when, adjudged guilty of treason and murder, Brown was hanged at Charlestown December 2.

He had admired the old man for his ideals and his courage, but could not condone the Harper's Ferry raid. In many respects, Barney thought, he was like William Walker, the filibuster leader. Both were fanatics with extravagantly preposterous aims too vast for their capabilities, and both came to the same end.

Although still confined to his home from the effects of the attack by Preston Brooks, Senator Sumner had been re-elected, this time on the Republican ticket, and Barney heard from him frequently. The political pot was about to boil over. President Buchanan was seeking to appease the slave states in an effort to stave off secession or civil war.

Several years earlier Henry Ward Beecher's sister, Harriet Beecher Stowe, had come out with her *Uncle Tom's Cabin*, stirring public sentiment against slavery. John Brown's raid tended to bring war closer. In spite of these and other indications, few persons in Chicago were prepared for or expected actual war.

The public generally seemed to feel that the slave states were using the threat of secession as a club to gain more favorable legislation. The worst that most leaders foresaw was the peaceful secession of the slave states, and while the majority regretted the break-up of the Union, a great many felt that both sides would be better off if the South seceded and formed a separate government.

Few expected war except Barney, for long ago he had worked an equation convincing him that hostilities were inevitable.

Now he took out his pencil and worked it again, but this time he possessed more known factors; *Uncle Tom's Cabin* and Harper's Ferry, for example. He entertained not the slightest doubt of the certainty of war although, since there still remained a few unknown factors, he was unable to determine the exact date.

Would the Democratic convention split the party wide open

and hand the election to the Republicans by default. Would the Republicans nominate Seward, as seemed likely?

As soon as he had the answers to these questions, Barney felt that he would have all the necessary known factors and could work out his equation and reach an exact answer.

By Christmas Wagoner's mill was rebuilt, and then was destroyed by fire a second time. Again, none could prove the slavery sympathizers responsible. Wagoner's editorials in the *Citizen* had become even more unbridled, and it had become widely known that he was Jack Jones, the Chicago Underground agent, although Barney actually operated the station. Perhaps the squalling baby in John Brown's last shipment had aroused suspicion. Perhaps the flood of publicity had brought matters to a head.

Except for the one occasion when the overflow had been hid in Wagoner's mill, all the runaways had been kept in Barney's barn. Financially Wagoner was virtually wiped out. He still retained his job on the *Cititzen,* but had lost all his savings of the preceding ten years and had become disheartened.

But Barney owned the livery barn and retained most of his Nicaragua profits. He had been little more than making expenses in the livery business and was far from satisfied. He kept seeking a means of bettering himself.

He could foresee little future in the livery business and abandoned the idea of the barber shop since it offered little for a man of destiny, the only person in the world to master the law of positivities. What he was seeking he finally found in the lightning-rod business. A white promoter named Lansing offered to let him in on the ground floor.

Lightning rods, he explained, were as much a necessity as food or clothing. The market was scarcely scratched. Profit on each rod was eight hundred per cent, installed. In a year or two the lightning-rod company would be rolling in riches. Barney could buy a controlling interest for — well, how much did he have?

He hesitated to admit to Julia that he had put all his remaining funds in the lightning-rod deal, for he planned to surprise her when the profits began to roll in. He was still dreaming of owning a mansion where he could stand on the gallery and shake hands with whites who would call him Mister Ford. Where he erred was in failing to work out an equation, so he would know what he was getting into. Of course he never laid eyes on the promoter again, nor on a cent of his investment.

Except for his sorry little livery business, he was, like Wagoner, almost penniless, but he was far from being daunted. After all, anyone with the ability to peer into the future, as he was convinced he could do with his law of positivities, was certain to accomplish much.

Meanwhile the traffic of the Underground was declining steadily. War sentiment was gaining constantly in the South, and the slaves were well aware of it. Why should they risk the bloodhounds and the Fugitive Slave Law when by waiting perhaps a year the war would set them free?

Chicago seemed to take less interest in the political possibilities than in the news of the new gold discoveries in the Pikes Peak country. It was like the California boom days all over again. Gold-seekers were finding nuggets in the streams and getting rich overnight. Horace Greeley was writing glowing articles in the New York *Tribune* describing his visit to the gold fields at Jackson's Bar and Gregory Gulch.

It was inevitable that Barney should succumb to another relapse of the gold fever. Except for his illness in Nicaragua, he might have gone on to California and become wealthy by this time; or so he thought. He began to read up on the Pikes Peak country and presently found himself unable to talk of anything else.

Julia failed to share his enthusiasm. For one thing, she was expecting a baby, and did not propose to have it on a sandbar in some God-forsaken wilderness. She expected to remain in Chicago, and if he was deluded enough to go chasing rainbows in the Great American Desert he could go it alone and she would join him when he struck it rich. Her attitude differend markedly from what it had been when they had departed for the California gold fields together, but doubtless the expected baby accounted for her change of heart.

Wagoner was much of the same mind as Julia, although for another reason. Now forty-three years old and not too sturdily built, he doubted that he would last long working with a shovel. Moreover, he knew nothing about gold mining. Someone must remain behind to operate the Underground station, even though the traffic was dwindling.

And if war came, he proposed to do some fighting if they would let him. He decided to remain in Chicago, at least until Barney surveyed the opportunities in the gold fields, and then perhaps he would follow if the prospects appeared promising.

Barney spent some time finding a buyer for the livery business, but finally sold out for $2,200. He divided it with Julia and hid his share in a money belt because prices were high in the gold fields and sometimes one failed to strike it rich for a month or so.

He was thirty-eight years old when he boarded the train for the Missouri River, but he entertained not the slightest doubt that he was to find wealth in the gold fields. His confidence was based on the repeated answers produced by his law of positivities.

VIII

His journey across the plains afforded Barney an ideal opportunity to test the efficacy of his algebraic system. His first known factor was the time, April of 1860, which he set down as known factor *a*.

By mid-month he was cooking for an emigrant party, half-way to Pikes Peak. The Democrats were holding their convention at Charleston and breaking up into factions. The Republicans were not to meet until May, but the nomination of Seward seemed assured. But more important to Barney's personal problem was the fact that gold had been discovered in the Pikes Peak region a year previously.

The next known factor was the place, which he designated as *b*. It was the spot in Nebraska Territory where the Oregon Trail crossed Sand Creek, twelve days west of Leavenworth by ox team.

To guard against Indian attacks at night, the train of twenty-two covered wagons was drawn up in a circle. The horses and oxen were grazing in the creek bottoms, and a lookout had been posted on the bluff above to watch for redskins.

The sun had just sunk behind the sandhills and in the circle of wagons half a dozen cook fires were burning and the air was filled with the aroma of antelope steaks and bacon sizzling in the frying pans, mingling with the sour smell of burning cottonwood stobs.

Next he came to *c*, the first human factor. Dode, in his twenties, with a month's growth of black whiskers, would have been called "white trash" in his home state of Georgia. He was loudly pro-slave and anti-Union. On one hip he carried a holstered Navy pistol and on the other a sheathed Bowie knife.

In the twelve days since the wagon train had departed from Leavenworth he had made himself spokesman for the Southerners who made up two-thirds of the party. Since Barney had set down Dode as known factor c, the group of Southerners could be designated only as c^4.

The next human factor was d, his name was Anse and he came from western Pennsylvania by way of bleeding Kansas. He was a year older than Dode, slow of speech, stockily built, wheat-blond, and ordinarily placid. When outriding he carried a long squirrel rifle across his pommel, but no side-arms. Had it not been for his father, Anse would have remained of little consequence in the wagon train.

A circuit-riding preacher, the old man was a dyed-in-the-wool abolitionist who never missed an opportunity to proclaim that slavery was accursed of God, a statement calculated to exasperate Dode and his Southerners. He might have been less bombastic had not his son been ready to back his father's statements with his fists.

Anse had some backing from the Northern minority in the wagon train, all of whom Barney lumped together in the equation as d^2.

Lizzie Ross, age 22, from Indiana, known factor e, wore a poke bonnet and except for a scattering of freckles, was quite attractive. She smiled and fluttered her long brown lashes first at Anse and then at Dode, which in no way made for harmony in the party.

She had no intent to be a trouble-maker or a dividing factor but, as if the slavery question were not sufficient to divide the emigrants into factions, she all unaware became a common divisor, all of which Barney set down algebraically as

$$\frac{c^4 \times d^2}{e}.$$

The next human factor was the grizzled old frontiersman and wagon train guide, Sorepaw Beck, who had guided a dozen trains across the Great American Desert, some as far as Oregon.

A few days earlier he had been bit by a rattlesnake and had been left behind at Fort Kearny in the care of an army doctor.

The lack of his frontier experience could prove to be an important factor in determining whether Barney and the others would reach the gold country alive, and in the equation he appeared as $-f$.

The wagon train had proceeded without a guide, and now was in charge of Uriah Coventry, the wagon boss. As a leader he was merely passable. Barney put him down as known factor g.

Known factor h was Barney himself, cooking his way to the gold fields in return for free transportation. The emigrants noted that their mulatto cook carried himself erect and looked them squarely in the eye. This habit irritated Dode, the Georgian, who felt that a black man who did not slouch or shamble was somehow disrespectful, and if he looked one in the eye he was putting on airs. What's more, the cook used words that Dode was unable to understand, and his speech was precise and unslurred. Back in Georgia, said Dode, they would take a blacksnake to a nigger who set himself up above white folks thataway.

Many Negroes got along with the whites by playing the clown, for they knew that everyone feels superior to a clown. But Barney never clowned, never made himself obtrusive, and most of the time his lips were parted to show white teeth in a friendly smile. At first everyone accepted him, like one of the oxen, as a useful but incidental part of the emigrant train.

With his problem set down on paper, Barney could foresee trouble breeding between factors c and d, Dode and Anse, leading to worse trouble between c^4 and d^2. It could be touched off by the divisor e, Lizzie Ross, or by h, the mulatto cook.

Then he considered another factor, a hypothetical one that he designated x. It represented the Indians lurking somewhere behind the bluffs. If they remained there, perhaps x would not become relevant to the problem, in which case the wagon boss, g, likewise could be eliminated. But if x came charging out from behind the bluff and wearing war paint, it followed that necessarily he would be forced to take into account the absence of wise old Sorepaw, factor $-f$.

Barney was squatting by his cook fire, thrusting fresh cottonwood under the frying pan and raking coals on the lid of the Dutch

Barney L. Ford, born a slave, made
and lost a half dozen fortunes in
Nicaragua and in Colorado and
Wyoming; he was credited with
changing the history of a state
and electing a President of the
United States. *Top photo courtesy
Denver Public Library Western
Collection. Center photo, cour-
tesy State Historical Society of
Colorado. Bottom photo from col-
lection of Fred and Jo Mazzulla.*

Greytown, Nicaragua, as rebuilt after bombardment which destroyed Barney Ford's United States Hotel. *Library of Congress Photo.*

Barney L. Ford's first business venture in Denver was a barber shop (to the right of barber pole) adjoining Heatley & Chase's gambling house on Denver's Blake Street. At the Platte House, earlier known as the Hemenway House, Ford worked for his room and board as a porter. *Denver Public Library Western Collection.*

The People's Restaurant, built by Barney L. Ford following the great fire of 1863, for several years was Denver's
outstanding eating establishment. *Denver Public Library
Western Collection, from advertisement in* Rocky Mountain News *September 1, 1863.*

In the seventies Barney L. Ford operated Ford's Hotel (arrow), formerly the Sargent House, at 1626 Larimer Street, Denver. *Denver Public Library Western Collection.*

Denver's Inter-Ocean Hotel was built by Barney L. Ford in 1873 and was still standing ninety years later. The picture shows the omnibuses, each drawn by four white horses, that met all the trains. *Collection of Fred and Jo Mazzulla.*

overnor John Evans f the Territory of Colorado, whose stand n the race issue may ave cost him a seat in he United States Sen- te. *Photo by M. B. rady & Co., from Den- er Public Library estern Collection.*

Jerome B. Chaffee, later United States Senator, was Territorial Delegate to Congress when Colo- rado, after eliminating a race discrimination provision from her con- stitution, was admitted to statehood. *Denver Public Library Western Collection.*

Colorado achieved state- hood after pink-cheeked William N. Byers, pub- lisher of the *Rocky Mountain News*, swung his support to Barney L. Ford's campaign against race discrimina- tion. *Denver Public Library Western Col- lection.*

Advertising card of Denver's Inter-Ocean Hotel, built by Barney L. Ford in 1873. *Courtesy Inter-Ocean Hotel, Denver.*

According to a legend which Barney L. Ford denied, he built this home at Breckenridge, Colorado, with gold dust recovered from a cache buried twenty years earlier. *Denver Public Library Western Collection.*

INTER-OCEAN HOTEL,
CHEYENNE, WYOMING.
B. L. FORD, - - - - - -, PROPRIETOR.

This House is new, with large and well ventilated rooms, all elegantly furnished. Electric Bells connecting all rooms with the office. All trains stop from thirty minutes to four hours, and everybody takes meals at the Inter-Ocean. Free 'Bus to all trains.

Barney L. Ford built the Inter-Ocean, Cheyenne's most pretentious hotel, but it bankrupted him. *Denver Public Library Western Collection.*

oven when Dode straddled a nearby wagon tongue and observed offhand:

"If they's one thing I can't stand, it's an uppity nigger. This cook is the first nigger ever I see, talks like a God damned college professor, or something. Putting on airs over his betters. I don't go for such doings."

Accustomed to such harassment, Barney was prepared to ignore it, but the wagon boss took it up.

"Ever stop to think, Dode, that maybe this nigger really is a college professor? How about it, Barney? Damn your hide, you been hiding something from us?"

Without looking up from his pots, Barney showed his white teeth in an easy smile.

"No, sir, not a professor, Mister Coventry. Just an M.A. Harvard, '57. *Cum laude.*"

Except in a general way he was uncertain of the meaning of *cum laude*, but as it turned out, none of the dozen hungry nearby emigrants knew, either; not even the circuit-riding preacher. Everyone chuckled except Dode, for in a way the joke had been turned on him. He scowled at Barney and spat in the dust.

"He better not pull any of that Harvard stuff on me, see, or I'll gnaw his guts out. I'm from Georgia, I am, and I don't take that kind of guff from any nigger."

Carswell, the lame Illinois farmer, seemed uneasy at the turn of the situation. "Don't do any gnawing till we reach the diggings, Dode. Barney's the best damn cook west of The River, but if you keep on bullyragging him he's like to put rat poison in our stew."

The Georgian might have let the matter drop had it not been for Lizzie, who slid feet first over the tail gate of her wagon, bonnet hanging down her back by its ribbons. When she smiled and fluttered her eyes at Dode and switched her skirts, he muttered, "Just wait till we get to Denver City and I'll learn this brash coon his place."

Now the circuit-riding preacher spoke up. "Denver City is in Kansas Territory and bless God, Kansas is due to be free soil, soon as the people vote on the constitution. The accursed blight of slavery will be outlawed from this promised land and then, my friend, this colored boy will have the same rights that you and I have."

Barney hoped that Anse's father knew what he was talking about and felt that he did, to judge from the Chicago newspapers.

He had hoped to take a stagecoach and beat these slow-moving emigrants to the gold country, but when he sought to buy a coach ticket at Leavenworth he discovered that the color line existed even out here on the plains. So it was that he came to be cooking his way with the emigrant train.

His money belt contained twelve hundred and sixteen dollars, which he surmised was more cash than any white man in the train carried with him, but Jim Crow had ruled that it was insufficient to buy him a stagecoach ticket.

Dode blazed up, "Reverend, you God damned nigger lovers are the ruination of this country. Next thing you'll be slobbering over the poor downtrod Indians, that never done nobody no harm excepting to massacre and scalp white women and children. Wouldn't put it past you."

"My friend, for two years I labored in the vineyard in bleeding Kansas." Beginning to show signs of spirit, the circuit rider shook a bony finger at the Georgian. "Shoulder to shoulder with John Brown, fighting the good fight for freedom for all God's children. Mind you, with John Brown himself, a saint if there ever was one."

"Saint?" Dode spat and laughed and spat again. "That murdering old nigger stealer? I'd of been plumb proud to help yank the rope that hanged him, I would. Reverend, you damned old psalm-singing idiot, you better keep your blathering to yourself if you want to steer clear of trouble."

Up to now stocky Anse, stowing buffalo chips in the cowhide swung beneath his wagon, had kept silent, but a deeper red now spread across his sun-peeled face.

"You take that back, Dode." His eyes narrowed. "You take back what you said about my pa."

"All right, I take it back." The Georgian laughed. "I'm wrong. Come to think about it, I never heard your pa sing a psalm."

The incident might have ended except for the circuit rider.

"And the wrath of God shall descend upon him who oppresseth his brethren. Woe unto him who holdeth God's children in bondage, and wieldeth the lash and trompeth down the downtrod. Everlasting torment in the uttermost depths of hell awaiteth him, and if there's any doubt about who I'm talking about, Brother Dode, I mean you."

The Georgian's face became Indian-red. "The hell you say, Reverend. Now, that kind of talk is something I don't take from nobody. Why, you damned old meddlesome goat, I got a good notion to give you a poke right in the nose. If you wasn't crowding Methusaleh, I'd sure as hell —"

"Hold on a second, Dode." Anse straightened, slicing hands together to brush away the dust of the buffalo chips. "If there's any poking to be done, you can start in on me. Likely you figure you're a rip-snorter, but to me you're just piddling white trash. So if you're of a mind to, just step up and take what's coming to you, or else button your lip."

Dode caught sight of Lizzie casting an admiring glance at Anse under her fluttering lashes and was stirred to action. Crouching, hand hovering over his holster, he edged about the fire.

Having started something that no one but his son could finish, the preacher retreated into the half-gloom behind the fire to watch and pray. The wagon boss maneuvered about behind Dode and snatched the pistol from its holster and the knife from its sheath.

The two sparred for a moment. Anse swung and missed, Lizzie squealed, the circuit rider dropper to his knees to pray, and Barney moved his pots and pans to the side of the fire so the victuals would remain warm without burning.

Dode darted forward and with a blow to the cheek set Anse back on his heels. The Southerners who were backing the Georgian raised a rebel yell that seemed to echo and echo down through the cottonwoods in the bottoms, growing louder and louder until it was a roar and at the same instant everyone realized that it was the drumming of hoofs that caused the roar, and the wagon boss called out, "Stampede! Everybody out!"

Forgetting their quarrel, Dode and Anse made a break with

the other menfolk, dashing through the gaps between the circled wagons to round up the frightened livestock. Almost immediately Carswell, the lame farmer, limped back into the firelight, a blank look on his face as he tugged at the arrow piercing his thigh and muttered:

"Lame in both legs now. Hell of a note!"

Those who had dashed out after the horses abruptly changed their minds and came pouring back through the gaps between the wagons, shouting, "Indians! Indians! Get your guns, boys!"

The wagon boss was complaining loudly because the lookout had failed to sound the alarm. He was unaware that the lookout lay dead with three arrows through his body, having been posted on the bluff where old Sorepaw never would have placed him, to constitute a perfect skylighted target.

Barney dived for the wagon where his belongings were carried but was forced to wait for the circuit rider, who was tugging at his Hawken rifle. Weapon in hand, Barney squatted behind a sack of flour leaning against a wagon wheel. He could see nothing at which to shoot, but heard a chilling, quavering yell somewhere in the darkness.

Everyone was shouting so that none could hear the orders of the wagon boss. The womenfolk had followed the instructions laid down by old Sorepaw at the beginning of the journey, and had hid in the wagons. Several minutes elapsed before the defenders were ranged about inside the circle of wagons, prepared to repel an attack.

Barney remained unfrightened, largely because of his confidence in the law of positivities, from which he had gained assurance that he would live to get rich in the gold fields.

Nevertheless, when an arrow thudded into a nearby wheel hub and buzzed for an instant like a rattlesnake, he broadened his barricade with another sack of flour.

Crouching behind a barrel, Anse was firing away into the darkness with his squirrel rifle. Dode was shooting, too, at no particular target, for the Indians failed to attack.

At length, for lack of anything at which to shoot, the emigrants ceased firing. The yelling from beyond the circle of wagons had ceased, too. Dode was beginning to boast that they had driven the red devils away. From her hiding place in the wagon Lizzie called out to ask if anyone knew what had happened to the lookout.

Except when the wagon boss had damned him for failing to sound the alarm, no one had chanced to think of the lookout. To show off before Lizzie, Dode said he wasn't the kind to leave the lookout out there at the mercy of those bloodthirsty savages, and by God he was going to rescue him.

Anse remarked that this was what he had been on the point of doing. Someone suggested that everyone go, and the rescuers fanned out and called that help was coming. Since he had not been invited, Barney remained behind.

Apparently there had been only five or six young Sioux braves in the war party, not enough to attack the wagon train and massacre the emigrants, but enough to raid the horse herd. So two had taken positions beyond the circle of wagons to distract attention by shooting a few arrows and shouting, while the others killed the lookout and stampeded the horses.

One young brave yearned to kill someone so he could count a coup for his coup stick, and knowing that sooner or later the whites would come out to learn the fate of the lookout, he hid behind a clump of sagebrush and waited.

Eager to play the hero before Lizzie, Anse was first to work his way up a chimney in the bluff. When he thrust his head above the rim he saw the young brave aiming an arrow at one of the rescuers scrambling up the face of the bluff.

When Anse's bullet struck him the Sioux leaped in the air and toppled over the bluff. All the whites rushed up and riddled the body of the fallen redskin. They found the Indian to be all of fifteen years old.

Strangely, the bowstring had been drawn taut at the instant the bullet struck the young brave, so the arrow had sped on and plowed into the earth a few feet from Dode, so everyone except the Georgian patted Anse on the back and told him he had saved Dode's life.

After finishing arguing about who was to get the choicest souvenirs from the body of the Indian boy, they started back to the wagons to tell the women how Anse had saved Dode, and then someone remembered that they had forgot about the lookout, so they climbed to the top of the bluff and what they found sobered them considerably.

They carried the lookout's body back to the wagons and covered it with a tarpaulin so it would spoil no appetites and asked Barney if he could serve supper before they dug the grave.

Everyone expected Dode to shake the hand of Anse in gratitude, but he had detected Lizzie fluttering her eyes at Anse. The circuit rider's son leaned his squirrel rifle against a wagon and clouted the ear of the man whose life he was credited with saving, but this time the rest of the emigrants joined in stopping the fight.

In the morning they discovered that the Indians had attempted to drive the stolen horses across the creek two miles downstream, but every last animal had bogged down in the sand and mud, with one scrawny Indian pony to boot.

The circuit rider attributed the salvation of the wagon train to the power of prayer, but Barney could have foretold, at least so far as he himself was concerned, how the affair would turn out. From the time that he had worked it all out on paper he had positive knowledge that he was due to get through alive, and now he knew that he was to become rich in the Pikes Peak country.

Had he carried his calculations further, he might have learned that he, a runaway slave, was to be the means of electing one president of the United States and of keeping another president in office; of so controlling the destiny of a Territory that he could block its admission into the Union until he gave his assent.

IX

William Green Russell came from Lumpkin County, Georgia, where Barney had worked in the Auraria gold fields. A victim of the gold fever, he had crossed the plains to California with the Forty-niners, but failed to make his expenses. The following year he returned, panning every stream along the north edge of what was to become known as the Pikes Peak fields, but without finding a trace of color.

A red-head Georgia mule skinner, John H. Gregory, had been bit by the gold bug in the Georgia fields and he, too, found his way to the Rocky Mountains. George A. Jackson, not a native of Georgia, came down with the fever merely from reading the headlines.

Years earlier, in Georgia, the claim adjoining Big Thompson's had been worked by Cherokees. Later some of these Indians crossed the plains to the California gold fields. On one of their California trips a party of these Cherokees had panned a small amount of dust from Ralston Creek, a few miles from the junction of Cherry Creek and the South Platte, where Denver City was to spring up so soon. Upon their return to Georgia they were unwise enough to boast of their discovery.

Russell heard their story and in 1858, with a few friends, joined the Cherokees on their return to the Rockies. A year earlier, on an expedition to pacify the Indians, a detachment of soldiers camped at the mouth of Cherry Creek. Later one of its Delaware guides rashly displayed a pouch of dust and nuggets he claimed to have panned from the sandbars near the army bivouac. Another party of gold-seekers employed him to take them to the spot, but he fell from his pony and suffered a fractured leg and since he had disclosed the location of his find they proceded without him.

So all at once several parties of gold-seekers were converging on the Pikes Peak country, including many who had been left jobless by the panic of 1857.

It was Jackson who made the original placer strike at Jackson's Bar on Clear Creek, then known as Vasquez Fork. At almost the same time Russell found gold in nearby Russell Gulch, and then Gregory uncovered the first fissure vein known in the Pikes Peak country, the Gregory Lode.

Within a few weeks the mountains were swarming with gold-seekers. By the end of the summer they had established two fair-sized towns. The town at the scene of the strikes was called Mountain City. The other, at the mouth of Cherry Creek, for a time rejoiced in two names.

South of the creek it was known as Auraria, after the place where most of the Georgians had gained their experience. North of the creek it was Denver City, named after General James W. Denver, governor of Kansas, although the boomers who founded the town were uncertain whether it lay in Kansas Territory.

By May 18, 1860, the date of Barney's arrival, Denver City's log cabins and tents were spreading in all directions. In the cottonwoods on the banks of the Platte at the mouth of Cherry Creek was a half-moon of Arapahoe tepees. Unlike the Indians Barney had known in Nicaragua, these Arapahoes were tall, dark, and hatchet-faced.

So far as he was concerned, Denver City was nothing more than a stopover, for like all the other gold-seekers, he was eager to reach Mountain City where the rich strikes had been reported. He hoped to get the jump on the covered wagon travelers by completing the journey to the diggings by stagecoach, but when he sought to buy a ticket at the log cabin Hinckley Express office he discovered that here, too, he was barred because of his color.

He arranged for transportation with a wagon train in return for his services as a barber. Denver City had sprung up on the plains at the foot of the Rockies, but he found the cabins of Mountain City clinging to steeple-steep mountainsides.

His aim in heading for the Pikes Peak country was to get in on the ground floor, but when he reached Gregory Diggings at Mountain City, he found the ground floor packed with six thousand other gold-seekers.

A mulatto could not rent a room in either of the log cabin hotels, and he was directed to Aunt Clara Brown, a laundress and the first of her race in the gold camp. She was fifty-eight years old and had washed her way to the diggings. Once a slave in Missouri, her husband and children had been sold before her last master died and left a will freeing her.

She had come to the diggings in 1859 and, charging fifty cents for washing a shirt, had saved more than a thousand dollars and was planning to buy the freedom of her husband and children.

Now that the Republicans had nominated Lincoln instead of Seward and Barney knew war to be inevitable, he fully expected the North to triumph within a few months and then the slaves would be freed.

He passed on this appraisal to Aunt Clara and advised her against buying freedom for her kinfolk since doubtless they would soon be freed anyway. She thanked him and told him he could sleep free of charge in her woodshed until he found a job.

With so much cash in his money belt Barney was seeking no job, but was all eagerness to stake out a claim and get rich. Beginning where Gregory had made his strike, he struck out down the gulch and tramped all the remainder of his first day without discovering a foot of ground that had not been staked off.

Undismayed, the following day he worked his way over the ridge and all the way down to Vasquez Fork, where Jackson had made his placer discovery at Jackson's Bar. Still he found every claim for miles up and down the creek already taken up, and it came to him that he was wasting his time tramping over the hills when he should be examining the maps at the district claim agent's office to discover what land was unclaimed.

Down in the valley he came upon two colored boys, Willis and Morrison, working a Long Tom. When they told him they were slaves owned by a Georgian, he asked them why they didn't run away.

97

Having worked for the Underground, he knew how to aid them. Mountain City lay in Nebraska Territory and Denver City in Kansas Territory, and a few miles to the west on the far side of the snowy range lay Utah Territory. In these mountains they could lose themselves easily, and if their master set the law on them, they could cross over the line into another Territory. At first they were in favor of it, but feared to take the big step without considering it more fully.

They told him he was wasting his time looking for placer ground, since everything was taken up for miles around. The knowing ones, like Gregory, were going in for lode mining, for within about a year all the sandbars would be worked out.

The following day Barney visited the claim office and studied the plats. He heard considerable talk about the Bowman strike on the ridge south of Mountain City, and after inspecting it and talking with Bowman he measured off two claims, set down his stakes and registered his entry at the office, one in Julia's name. They are recorded at the Gilpin County courthouse in the claim book of the Illinois Central District as numbers 6 and 7 west of discovery.

Immediately he wrote to Julia that it was but a matter of time until they would be rich, and he wrote Wagoner urging him to drop everything and come west without delay so he, too, could get in on the ground floor.

He employed a disillusioned prospector to build a cabin and windlass, hired a helper, and began sinking a shaft at what appeared to be a likely spot to cut in on an extension of the Bowman Lode. Before long they encountered solid rock, necessitating blasting. By the time they were down forty feet he had spent eight hundred of his twelve hundred dollars and still had found no gold.

Just before Wagoner was due to arrive at Denver City, a group of armed men appeared at his claim and at gunpoint their leader ordered Barney to get the hell out of there.

Claiming to be a lawyer, he insisted that, while the law authorized a Negro to own real estate, it prohibited him from filing on a homestead or mining claim, so consequently Barney's filing was illegal. The leader claimed to have made a white man's legal filing on it and warned Barney that he was trespassing. The claim jump-ers gave him five minutes, to use in packing his belongings or in digging his own grave.

X

When Wagoner arrived in Denver August 1, 1860, he was met by a disheartened Barney who was bitterly resentful of the high-handed methods of the claim jumpers. However, Wagoner brought him news that sent his spirits soaring, for now Barney was the father of a boy born July 2 and named Louis Napoleon by Julia.

While awaiting Wagoner's arrival, Barney had become acquainted with a twenty-four-year-old mulatto, E. J. Sanderlin, operator of a barber shop on Denver's Larimer Street. He told Barney he was the son of Wilson Sanderlin, a wealthy Briton living in New Orleans who, in common with many other white men, maintained two families and two homes. One wife was white and the other, E. J. Sanderlin's mother, was black.

Upon the death of the father the black branch of the family had sued to break the will leaving his entire fortune to his white wife and children. They won a judgment, and young Sanderlin's share of the estate was $30,000. Most of his heritage had been lost in California mining speculations, and he had come to Denver June 11, 1859, being one of the earliest settlers.

Barney's account of the loss of his property to the claim jumpers left him sympathetic, but he remarked that the newcomer had gained some cheap experience. He had no means of knowing how much Barney had sunk in his unfortunate mining venture, and could not guess that his money belt still contained some four hundred dollars.

"Anybody with a twenty-dollar grubstake can buy a pan or build himself a Long Tom and start making money the very first day," he observed.

"But lode mining takes capital. You can easy put twenty thousand dollars into the ground before tapping a vein. And where is a colored man going to get that kind of money?"

Sanderlin had an eighth grade schooling and used reasonably good English. Barney had some knowledge of placer mining, but none whatever of lode mining.

Sanderlin said: "Last summer Will H. Iliff and some others crossed the continental divide into Utah Territory and found a showing of gold on the Blue River. If you're smart, Barney, you'll take a job in my barber shop, but if you still expect to get rich quick, why don't you head for the Blue before the big stampede starts? It's near a town called Breckenridge."

Barney could foresee no future in barbering for someone else. Still having money in his belt, by the time Wagoner arrived he was breathlessly impatient to try his luck at Breckenridge.

While working for the Underground Wagoner had faced prison and had taken many risks, but his two destructive fires had left him apprehensive and uncertain. Gold-seeking was foreign to his experience, and after hearing how Barney's claim had been jumped his doubts seemed amply justified. He would say only that he would think it over, for there seemed less risk in operating a barber shop at Mountain City. Who ever heard of claim-jumpers grabbing a barber shop?

Barney worked out another equation, but was balked by an unknown factor; the inability of a colored man to hold title to a mining claim. He consulted a lawyer.

"All you have to do is file the claim in my name, Barney. After you mail me the legal description I'll send you papers showing that you're entitled to keep eighty per cent of everything you take from it."

Barney was grateful for the advice. He took Wagoner with him on his return to Mountain City, and his friend found a cabin he could rent for a barber shop and definitey renounced the opportunity to get rich quick.

Barney sought out the two slaves, Willis and Morrison, and offered them day wages if they would run away and join him in searching for gold at the new camp at Breckenridge, and although doubtful at first, they finally were persuaded.

They were to make the break a day in advance so Barney would not be suspected of aiding them, and were to wait at the forks of the Vasquez until he joined them with pack burros and picks and shovels and food. His scheme worked out precisely as he had planned, although they suffered from cold the night they camped on 13,-000-foot Argentine Pass.

Barney was disappointed to find that three or four thousand gold-seekers had preceded him to Breckenridge, which already was a sizeable town boasting a log fort for protection against the Utes, and even a mint to coin the product of the sluices into five-dollar gold pieces. The camp had been named for Major Thomas E. Breckenridge, a member of the discovery party.

As had been the case at the Gregory Diggings, all the placer ground for miles along the Blue had been taken up, so, with two more colored boys he picked up at Breckenridge, Barney began working back up a fork in French Gulch.

Presently the party found a good showing of color, so Barney filed a claim in the name of the Denver lawyer and sent him the papers and with his four Negro employees set about building a cabin, for it was late in the summer and the winters were severe at this 10,000-foot elevation.

He wrote Julia that he had struck it rich at last, but advised her not to join him until the following summer, for she would be taking an unjustified risk in crossing the plains with the baby so late in the season, when raging blizzards might be expected.

The daily yield of their two Long Toms kept growing larger and larger and the dust grew deeper in the bottle Barney kept buried beneath the dirt floor of the cabin. By the first of September all the cash in his money belt was exhausted, so he took a sack of dust to the Breckenridge mint to exchange for gold pieces. While cashing his dust he encountered his erstwhile wagon train tormentor, Dode!

More disreputable in appearance than ever, the Georgian plainly was down on his luck. His only word to Barney was, "Howdy," but he was unable to take his eyes from the gold pieces. Uneasy,

Barney waited until nightfall, headed away from French Gulch and lost himself in the timber before doubling back to his claim.

For several days he was fearful of the possible results of his encounter with Dode, but nothing happened and the gold dust grew deeper in the buried bottle, and he was beginning to worry because he had failed to receive the papers the lawyer had promised to send him.

By the fifteenth of September fresh snow covered the mountain peaks, and each morning the creek was rimmed with ice. Then one afternoon the sheriff appeared and served him with ejectment papers sworn out by the Denver lawyer. The attorney was in possession of the claim papers Barney had filed in his name, and lacking the written agreement the lawyer had promised him showing the 80-20 arrangement, Barney found himself on the wrong side of the law.

The sheriff gave him twenty-four hours to pack his belongings and get out. Bitter and discouraged, he dug up his bottle of dust and the five disillusioned gold-seekers began packing without knowing where they were going or what their next step was to be.

Shortly after nightfall the question was decided for them by the sound of a party of horsemen clattering up the trail. When he heard the hoofbeats, Barney prudently thrust the bottle within his shirt and the five Negroes fled from the cabin into the timber.

The group of horsemen was led by Dode. Barney could hear him saying the damn niggers probably buried it under the cabin floor, and they dismounted and went inside and Barney could hear them cursing as they dug. Motioning his companions to follow, he struck out up the mountainside south of the creek. The climb through the timber in the darkness was cold and arduous.

Lacking a cabin, with winter approaching, without even bedding for camping, Barney reluctantly gave orders to return to Denver City. They dared not return to the cabin for bedding and food and their burros, so they made their way afoot over the mountains to Swan River settlement, where Barney parted with most of his dust in exchange for supplies sufficient to carry them back over the continental divide to Denver.

As the story of Dode's raid was noised about, the thwarted

raiders spread the report that the niggers had hid their gold dust in a secret cache on the mountainside.

First they said its value was a thousand dollars and then, as the story passed from mouth to mouth, it grew to be ten thousand and finally to a hundred thousand. Residents of the Breckenridge district fell into the habit of calling the mountain Nigger Hill, and the name began to appear on all the maps.

Miners who tired of working for wages would quit their jobs to prospect Nigger Hill for Barney's buried treasure, and in Breckenridge it was said that if these treasure-hunters had put in as much time working for wages as they spent searching for this supposed cache of buried gold dust, they would have earned more than the output of all the mines in the district.

Years later, when Barney actually became wealthy, this affair gave rise to the most fantastic rumors intended to account for the source of his riches.

When he returned to Denver City and paid off his helpers, Barney was penniless again, but still retained faith in his law of positivities despite his summer's misfortune. He was convinced that there was nothing inherently wrong with his system; temporary failures were due merely to the lack of unknown factors to set out with. Convinced that he was destined to acquire riches, he remained uncertain as to whether it was to be next week, next summer, or even later.

Swarming with emigrants headed for the gold fields, Denver City had been prospering during the summer months, but now it was subsiding into a winter recession. The peril of blizzards had brought wagon train traffic across the plains to an end, and already many disappointed "go-backers" had returned to "the states."

Like Barney, hundreds of jobless miners had drifted back to Denver City to wait until the warmth of spring melted the deep snows in the mountains and thawed the sandbars.

Most of Denver's log cabins were being replaced by one-story false fronts, unpainted and as yet unweathered. Few of the settlers had brought their families, so the female population was confined largely to the dance halls and sporting houses.

With business in the doldrums, Sanderlin was unable to make a place for Barney in his barber shop, but shortly the disappointed gold-seeker found a job as porter and bellboy at the modest frame Hemenway Hotel, separated by a fifteen-foot lot from Chase & Heatley's Progressive Club, the town's leading gambling hell. His payment was limited to room, board, and tips. He was unable to send money to Julia, who had resumed her chambermaid work in Chicago and was earning more than he.

Having been his own boss so long, operating hotels in Nicaragua and a livery business in Chicago, he was not content to work indefinitely for nothing but tips. He persuaded Sanderlin to sell him a barber chair and tools, to be paid for when business picked up.

By posting this equipment as security for his rent, he talked a jobless carpenter into building him a tiny frame shack on the fifteen-foot lot adjoining the gambling house, and at last found himself in the barber business.

Among his first customers was William N. Byers, a stocky young chap who was growing a beard to hide his spanked-baby pink cheeks. In his position dignity was highly essential, for he was owner, publisher, and editor of the Rocky Mountain *News,* recently converted from a weekly to a daily.

He was campaigning to persuade Congress to create a Territory in the Pikes Peak country, to be formed from parts of Kansas, Nebraska and Utah territories and to be known as Jefferson Territory.

Had the Mason and Dixon line been extended sufficiently to the west, it would have passed within a few miles of the Cherry Creek settlement.

At that time Congress was torn by controversy over the admission of new Territories in the growing West. The Northerners were violently opposed to the extension of slave territory, and the Southerners were determined to block the admission of free soil territory. The compromisers were striving for the admission of new territories in pairs, one free and one slave.

While Byers' beard was being trimmed, he proclaimed himself a Unionist Republican and an enemy of slavery and boasted that his staff included a Negro, Jack Smith, who operated his press. He told Barney to pass the word along to his colored friends and to inform them that subscriptions to the *News* were only a dollar a month, strictly in advance.

As a steward on the Mississippi and as a barber in Chicago, Barney had learned the asset value of his knowledge of the classics. He decided to try it on Byers.

> *"He who is fitted for heroic deeds*
> *Mother, although he be an African*
> *Or savage Scythian — he is noble born."*

The publisher was impressed. "Didn't know you were a poet, Barney. Keep on, and before you know it, you'll be good enough to get your poems printed in the *News,* free of charge."

Byers failed to leave a tip, but Barney was pleased to hear him say he was opposed to slavery — that is, until he read editorials in the *News* indicating that Byers and other promoters of Territorial status were planning to by-pass the slavery issue.

The bill to establish the proposed new Territory read: "That while slavery has no legal status in said Territory, nothing herein shall be construed to authorize or prohibit its existence herein."

As Barney saw it, the proposed measure was worse than none. Unless the proponents of Territorial status took a forthright stand against slavery, he might be forced into the choice he had made in Nicaragua, when William Walker's edict had compelled him to leave the country.

Denver City's most lavish tipper was Barney's neighbor, Ed Chase, one of the proprietors of the Progressive gambling establishment. Chase was a young man, grey before his time, a college classmate of Leland Stanford. Armed with a shotgun, he customarily sat on a high stool overlooking his tables, effectually discouraging any contemplation of cheating.

So far as Barney was concerned, this was hearsay, for he had never entered Chase's place. Back in his steamboating days, experience had taught him that crap shooting was not his calling, and while he enjoyed a friendly game of penny ante, he knew himself to be no match for the professional gamblers. Actually, however, he was barred from the Progressive by the color line. Only whites were permitted to lose their money to Ed Chase.

A college man, Chase was no tyro at quoting the classics, but found himself no match for Barney and finally admitted it. Being somewhat of a joker, he would bring his most learned customers into the barber shop and lay them even money that Barney could quote from any writer they chose to name.

Once Barney quoted a passage from the Bible when he should have quoted Wordsworth, but no one knew the difference and Chase won his bet.

The gambler claimed to believe in slavery, and as justification quoted a line from Horace about the cursed wretches enslaved to the vice of gambling. His jest buoyed Barney's spirits, for he had been feeling sorry for himself, but now he told himself that he was a free man while any number of whites actually were slaves since, when one got right down to cases, as Chase would say, the gambler was living off the product of their toil.

Chase conceded that only fools gambled, but since most of the human race were damned fools, who was he to keep a fool and his money from being parted? Anyone stupid enough to buck the law of probabilities deserved to lose his money.

As Barney became more closely acquainted with the gambler, he began to question him about the law of probabilities, since it had something in common with his law of positivities.

Chase claimed to operate a "square" house and said that everyone playing his wheels knew of the three per cent house cut. As Barney heard it, the cut was twenty per cent, but that was beside the point.

Barney's law of positivities was useless when applied to a game of chance, even though it provided a means of reasoning out the Unknown when certain known factors were present. But reason and known factors are of scant use in attempting to guess where the little roulette ball will come to rest, although almost anyone can calculate the odds for or against a given number.

The law of probabilities can tell what probably will happen in any game dependent upon sheer chance. But assuming that one made no error in the known factors, Barney's law of positivities could foretell positively what would happen in a given set of circumstances.

With seven horses in a race, all that the law of probabilities can reveal is that each stands one chance in seven of winning. But with all the known factors, Barney knew his law of positivities could tell him positively which horse would win.

But it was necessary to know far more than the known factors upon which the average bettor backs his judgment. Besides the past record of each entry, the weight he carries, the record of the jockey and the condition of the track, one must know which jockey had just quarreled with his sweetheart, which horse becomes listless when away from home, whether the owner is strapped for funds and is tempted to bet against his own entry, and countless other similar factors.

Ed Chase's law of probabilities was unable to tell him which player would break the bank at roulette, although it could come close to telling him in advance how much his games would yield in any given month.

On the other hand, Barney could prove by his law of positivities that he was to become rich, that there was to be a war, that the slaves were to be freed, and many other Unknowns, including information about God and the Hereafter.

XI

At the time of Barney's first appearance in Denver, no one knew the precise status of the members of his race in the Pikes Peak country, and because of the gold craze, few gave it a thought.

The Missouri Compromise had been emasculated so that the voters of Kansas and Nebraska could make their own decisions about slavery. Denver lay in Kansas Territory, and in 1859 a Kansas convention had drafted a proposed state constitution outlawing slavery, but as yet it had not been submitted to the voters.

The situation was almost identical in Nebraska Territory, which claimed the area north of Denver and east of the continental divide, including Mountain City, soon to be known as Central City.

West of the divide, in Utah, that Territory's organic act of 1850 limited the votes to whites, and the Mormon leader, Brigham Young, had issued a statement holding slavery to be a divine institution and maintaining that the black man was subject to the curse of Ham.

Moreover, a portion of the Pikes Peak country that soon was to be known as Colorado, lay within the borders of New Mexico Territory, which had been organized as slave territory in 1850.

It will be recalled that in 1857 the Supreme Court had ruled in the Dred Scott case that the black man possessed no rights that the white man was bound to respect and that Congress was powerless to outlaw slavery in the Territories.

President Buchanan had served notice on Congress that the government would protect the property right of owners bringing their slaves into the Territories.

Barney had written urgent protests to the leaders of the Anti-slavery movement; to Senator Sumner, William Lloyd Garrison, Gerrit Smith, Frederick Douglass, and many others. Most of the replies held to the opinion that the Territories retained the right to embrace or reject slavery.

So much time was necessary for mail to cross the plains that their letters were not received until Barney had told his friends, Willis and Morrison, that they were free because they were on free soil.

He was fearful that the court ruling and President Buchanan's stand were paving the way for the Pike's Peak country to become slave territory. The civil code of the proposed Territory of Jefferson would have barred "Indians, Negroes, mulattoes or black persons" from testifying in court.

Barney's shop was across the street from the log stagecoach station of the Leavenworth & Pikes Peak Express Co., and usually the barber shop was the first place sought by male coach passengers after their long trip across the plains.

Up the street a few doors was the fur trading post of the trapper and frontiersman, Ceran St. Vrain, who wore his hair long and probably had never been inside a barber shop.

On the far side of Ed Chase's gambling hall was the little frame Empire Bakery owned and operated by John J. Riethmann, a Fifty-niner. Searching for gold, he had found it in the baking business. He was a customer of the barber shop, and he and Barney became close friends and later engaged in several profitable business deals together.

With spring bringing a new flood of emigrants, Barney was prospering in a small way, but remained dissatisfied and spent many evenings working out equations.

Nearly a year previously his law of positivities had convinced him that he would find riches at Breckenridge. Now he worked the equation again and again, and each time the answer was the same; he positively was to become rich at Breckenridge.

One thing it failed to tell him was *when*; so he made up his mind that this coming summer was the time. Julia and little Louis Napoleon came from Chicago to join him, and he discussed the situation with her. Despite her faith in Barney, she felt that he

110

should waste no more time and money searching for gold. She wished him to return to the hotel business, at which he had been so successful in Nicaragua.

So he got out his pencil again and substituted another known factor, h, representing his knowledge of hotel keeping, for the previous known factor g, his knowledge of placer mining. The answer came out the same; he was to get rich at Breckenridge — and perhaps it meant in the hotel business. He wrote to his friend Wagoner at Mountain City and made arrangements with him to take over operation of the Denver barber shop.

The preceding summer he had spent most of his time at the diggings in French Gulch, and now he felt certain that no one at Breckenridge would identify him as the leader of the Negro miners that supposedly had hid their gold dust on Nigger Hill.

Inquiring about Dode, he learned that the Georgian had left town the same day the sheriff received a reward bulletin from his home state. Barney rented a frame shack, opened a boarding house for miners, and presently sent to Denver for Julia and Louis Napoleon.

Meanwhile, in February of 1861 a new bill providing for the organization of Colorado Territory had been passed by the Senate. Like the earlier bills, it sidestepped the slavery issue, but provided that "every free white male above the age of 21" should be eligible to vote at the first election, and that the Territorial Legislature should establish election laws thereafter.

Senator Stephen A. Douglas, leader of the Northern Democrats, chanced to be absent from the Senate chamber when the bill was passed, and the following day when he realized what had happened, demanded vociferously that the bill should be called back and reconsidered.

He charged that since the proposed new Territory of Colorado was to include a portion of the slave territory of New Mexico, Congress was attempting illegally to create free territory from slave territory. He claimed that it transgressed the rights of the New Mexicans living in that area.

Senator Green of Missouri maintained that the only residents

111

of the area were a few wandering Indians, and no blacks or whites, so no rights would be transgressed.

Douglas was voted down on his motion to reconsider, but all the heated debate on the slavery issue had much to do with arousing the public and stirring up war sentiment.

The Colorado Territory organic act was approved by President Buchanan February 28, but it left Barney puzzled. Since all whites were free, what was the notion of Congress in limiting the vote to *free* white males?

Kansas had become a free state a month earlier.

The governorship of the new Territory, a juicy political plum, paid $1,500 a year, plus $1,000 for services as Indian Agent of the Territory. President Buchanan left the appointment to Lincoln, who assumed office a few days after the measure was signed. Lincoln appointed William Gilpin.

At the time that Douglas was protesting the Colorado bill, the steamship *Star of The West* was fired upon while attempting to enter Charleston harbor with supplies for Fort Sumter. On April 12 Sumter fell to the Confederacy and the war became a reality, which failed to surprise Barney since he had worked it all out on paper and had been expecting it for some time.

The Western Union had been built only as far west as Julesburg, and the dispatch reporting the outbreak of war was rushed from the end of the telegraph line to Denver by pony express. When published in Byers' *News* it touched off not only an explosive controversy, but gunplay as well.

Southern sympathizers hoisted a Confederate flag over a store, but when armed Unionists marched down the street it vanished. Dick Whitsitt fought a duel with Park McLure, wounding him slightly. Lucien W. Bliss, secretary of the new Territory, and Dr. J. S. Stone duelled with shotguns at forty paces and the doctor was killed.

Since he was at Breckenridge, Barney missed the excitement, but his boarding house soon felt the impact of the strife. All the young men were returning to "the states" to join one cause or the other, and enlistments soon cut down emigration to the gold fields, so the expected Breckenridge boom did not materialize. Moreover, by this time the placer claims to a large extent had been worked out.

Nearly everyone in the district had been searching for gold, but from over the ridge in California Gulch came a storekeeper with a different idea. He filed two claims on the Thomas and Boren lodes in the Arazonia Silver Mining District near Breckenridge. They produced little or nothing, but his faith in silver ultimately made him the richest man in the West and won him a United States senatorship. His name was H. A. W. Tabor.

Late in the summer Barney received a letter from Wagoner, who had been offered a position in the East as assistant to a sutler with the Union army and who consequently wished to give up the Denver barber shop. Barney closed his Breckenridge boarding house and returned to Denver, still convinced that some day his equation would pay off and he would get rich at Breckenridge.

Julia could see little future in the barber shop, feeling that his Nicaragua experience fitted him better for the restaurant business. By this time they had saved a modest stake, so he bought the fifteen-foot barber shop lot and building on time payments and employed a carpenter to build a lean-to addition on the back, where he opened a lunch counter.

Even by the frontier town's standards, it was quite insigniflicant, but with Julia helping with the cooking and waiting on customers, they earned a modest profit.

Up to this time he had been interested mainly in his own economic problems, but now something more important began edging its way into his life.

He always carried himself with an air of dignity, was generally liked for his pleasant manner and intelligence, but he was far from being resigned to the discrimination and indignities to which he and his people were subjected by the whites. He had been cheated by a white confidence man in Chicago, by the white claim-jumpers at Mountain City, by the white lawyer who had swindled him of his placer claim at Breckenridge.

At the time there had been little that he could do about it, but he was left burning with resentment.

The census showed but eighty-nine colored persons in Colorado

Territory, of whom Barney, Wagoner, and Sanderlin were the only ones with even a moderate degree of education. They were hoping that the First Territorial Legislature, meeting in November, would grant them the vote. They turned naturally to Barney for leadership.

Now he possessed something more than his own selfish interest to spur him on, something bigger than himself. For the time being, he almost forgot about attempting to get rich as he plunged into the fight to win for his people equality of voting rights.

XII

Most of the political leaders were customers of Barney's shop, and he used his best efforts to persuade them to work and vote for equal rights for the colored man, but seemed to make scant progress.

Although many of the original gold-seekers had been pro-slavery men from Georgia, the bulk of the later emigration had come from the northern states, and now, as the demonstration following the news of the war's outbreak had shown, the majority were pro-Union.

He was bitterly disappointed when Publisher Byers failed to swing the support of the *News* behind the equal franchise movement.

"I'm a Unionist and all for freeing the slaves," he told Barney. "I believe in justice for the colored man, but the time just isn't ripe, Barney. If they were all college-educated, like you, I'd say give 'em the vote, but it would be a crime to let these ignorant Negroes vote when they can't even read."

Like many others, Byers assumed Barney to be a college man, and Barney saw no harm in permitting him to think so. The publisher's attitude was typical of that of most of the political leaders. It was heartbreaking to encounter that attitude so often: "I'm for justice and equal rights for the colored man, but . . . "

Almost invariably he found some qualification, some cagey hedging. He brought his arguments to bear chiefly on the Unionist Republicans. Lincoln was a friend of the colored man, and it was up to every loyal Republican to support him. Over and over he hammered away at this argument.

When the bill to regulate elections was introduced in the Legislature, it extended the vote to "every male person of the age of 21 and upwards," but immediately the Southern Democrats offered an amendment to limit the vote to whites. After lengthy debate the amendment was beaten down, as Barney had known it would be, for he had worked it out in advance by means of algebra.

He cast his first vote at the next election, and the day he cast his first ballot marked a milestone in his life. Strangely, one of the first to congratulate him was young, cagey, cautious, reticent Luther Kountze, a customer who abjured chit-chat in the barber chair. Even Barney's quotations had failed to thaw him.

He operated a little business in a frame shack on the corner, buying and selling gold dust, lending money and doing a general banking business. Barney had opened an account with him, but since he kept plowing his earnings back into better equipment, his balance seldom exceeded one hundred dollars.

Young Luther, in his mid-twenties, had come to Denver from Omaha, where he had worked in a bank owned by his brothers, Gus and Herman. Within five years the Kountze brothers were to establish a leading Wall Street banking house.

Chase and Heatley were reputed to be honest gamblers, and Luther Kountze enjoyed the reputation of being a "square" banker. He was in business to make money for Kountze Brothers and made no pretense of operating a charity.

Anyone who owed him money knew he must pay every last cent on the due date or face a lawsuit. Contrariwise, he could be depended upon to pay his debts promptly and in full; a good man to deal with, if one were honest.

Occasionally Jim Beckwourth, the noted mulatto frontiersman, would drift into town to visit his Mexican wife, whom he addressed as "Lady Beckwourth." Jim, who wore his hair long and was no boon to barbers, was in his sixties when he made his last visit to Denver, became involved in an argument with Will Payne, a blacksmith for the Holladay stage lines, and killed him.

For some years Jim had lived with the Crow Indians and had come to be regarded as a chief. In Denver in those days a suspect in a killing was seldom hanged unless the offense had been in connection with horse stealing, but public officials scrupulously followed the law and kept him in jail until he was tried and acquitted on the ground of self defense.

Jim had no wish to remain cooped up in jail, so he fled and joined the Crows again. The Indians were delighted at his return, for he had always brought the tribe good luck. They thought a lot of him, and didn't propose to lose him again.

So at length, according to legend, when he began talking nostalgically of civilization, they suspected that he was planning to desert them once more, so in his honor they arranged a huge feast of boiled dog and placed poison in his dog stew and killed him, and so managed to keep Jim Beckwourth with them forever. Actually, Jim died of food poisoning while on the trail two days before he was to rejoin the Crows.

Another early-day colored friend of Barney was Lewis Price, a runaway slave from Fredericksburg, Missouri. He had been an itinerant preacher, but upon reaching Denver engaged in the laundry business, which he found to be more profitable.

Often Barney received letters from his friend, Wagoner, who had been commissioned to recruit for the 29th Illinois colored regiment. Later he was commissioned by the governor of Massachusetts to recruit for the 5th Cavalry of that state.

Still later Governor Yates of Illinois commissioned him, with the rank of major, to enlist refugees and contrabands under a recent act of Congress. He served so efficiently that General Grant sent him a letter of commendation.

Meanwhile the war was bringing to the Pikes Peak country a new type of emigrant, the young man evading military service, and in later years it was said frequently that the pioneers who built Denver were draft dodgers.

There was a time when Barney contemplated following the example of Wagoner by joining the army, but Julia pointed out that he was forty-one years old, a man of property, and could not leave her to run the business, for she could find no one to operate the barber shop, and moreover she had all she could handle working at the lunch counter and caring for Louis Napoleon, and another baby coming.

They lived in a tiny room in the rear of the lunch counter lean-to. They were sound asleep at 2 o'clock on the morning of April 19, 1863, when a drunken guest overturned the stove in the Cherokee House and started a disastrous fire.

When Barney thrust his head from the door, he could see the crackling flames rolling overhead, fanned by a brisk wind. Already they had leaped F Street, and Kountze's little frame bank building on the corner was ablaze.

Barney called to Julia to get into her clothes and prepare to abandon the place. Quickly donning trousers and shoes, he grabbed three-year-old Louis, took Julia by the arm and dashed across lots to the Sanderlin home on Lawrence Street, then turned back to aid the firefighters swarming the streets.

Young Kountze was wearing shoes, but no trousers, and was carrying a drawer of papers from the bank and his flapping nightshirt was streaked with black. After carrying the records to safety in the brick Clark & Gruber mint, he returned to fight the fire.

The town marshal was striving to organize a bucket brigade to carry water from Cherry Creek, but found that the fire blocked the way to the creek. Gambler Ed Chase and his partner, Heatley, were shoveling sand on the roof of their gambling house to keep the sparks from getting a start, and they were heaving it on the roof of Barney's place, too. This was once when the color of a man's skin made no difference.

After saving the barber tools, Barney took his place with a shovel alongside the gamblers, the banker, and Riethmann, the baker. Already the little frame bank had gone up in flames and the Hemenway House was blazing.

Despite their desperate efforts, the fire swept along the street, and Barney watched his place go up in smoke along with the gambling house. They continued to shovel sand, but with little effect, and by sunrise virtually the entire business district had been destroyed.

Exhausted, Barney returned to Sanderlin's and learned that an hour earlier Julia had given birth to a daughter who was to be named Sarah Elizabeth. At first he was overjoyed and proud, but presently began to wonder how he was to feed another mouth, now that his business had been wiped out. He became so downhearted that he retired to the front parlor and rested his head on his folded arms and was on the verge of tears when Sanderlin appeared, begrimed from fire fighting, patted his shoulder, congratulated him, and offered him a job in his Larimer Street barber shop, which had come through undamaged.

Even after a breakfast of ham and eggs and coffee, Barney felt little better. Exhausted as he was, he was too nervous to sleep, so in mid-morning he returned to Blake Street to learn if anything might be salvaged.

When he came to the brick store building of Tootle & Leach, he made out a newly-painted sign, *Kountze Brothers Bank. Temporary Quarters Inside. Open for Business.* Upon entering he found young Luther Kountze, shaved, dressed, and as neat as ever, seated at a desk behind the pine board counter at the rear of the store between the dried apples and the cracker barrel.

"Morning, Barney," he called in his cagey, cautious voice. "And what can I do for you this morning?"

Barney informed him that he had dropped in to learn what chance there might be of borrowing sufficient funds to start up in business again.

The banker puckered his lips. "Any insurance?" The dejected Barney shook his head.

"What security have you?"

Nothing but his deposit in the bank, Barney told him; fifty dollars, perhaps. And his barber tools.

"Um-m." The banker frowned. "You own the lot on which the shop stood, don't you?"

Barney said he wasn't certain; he had been buying the lot and building on time and still owed four hundred dollars on the mortgage.

"Well, that fifteen-foot lot isn't worth more than fifty dollars, at the outside. Let's call it fifty, and add to it your fifty in the bank. Total, one hundred dollars, against a mortgage debt of four hundred. So actually you lack three hundred dollars of being worth nothing at all."

Barney was aware of a swelling in his throat. Admitting that Mister Kountze was right, he apologized for troubling him and reached for the hat he had borrowed from Sanderlin.

"Sorry, Barney." The banker turned away to gaze from the

window, tapping his teeth with his pen holder. "Sorry you saw fit to conceal some of your assets."

Dumfounded, Barney could only stare, wide-eyed. The banker went on: "You've got the best security in the world, Barney. Personal integrity. You pay your bills. People trust you. You're a first-rate businessman. You have shown that you know how to make money. How much would you like to borrow?"

Barney was so taken aback that he merely stood staring, mouth open. In all his life no white man had ever praised him so. He wondered if he dared ask to borrow a thousand dollars.

Impatient, Kountze frowned. "Well, how about five thousand? Ten thousand? On your personal note, understand?"

As soon as he could find his voice, Barney ventured that two or three thousand would be sufficient.

The banker shook his head. "Now, let me tell you something, Barney. You can't possibly get anywhere on that fifteen-foot lot; nothing much more than a bare living. You've got to build for the future, man. This town is growing. Why, some day Denver will have twenty-five thousand population; maybe thirty.

"You go out and find what it will cost you to build a first-class two-story building, and equip it, and I'll see that you get the money. Up to ten thousand; not a red cent more."

Barney stammered out his thanks, but the banker cut him off with:

"Don't thank me. This is an out-and-out business proposition. I expect to make money off of you. All I'll charge you for the loan is twenty-five per cent a year interest."

Barney was so confused that he scarce knew what to think as he made his way back to Sanderlin's to tell Julia the good news. Or was it good news?

Three times he had been swindled by white men. Was Kountze planning to trick him? Was the young banker merely contriving a practical joke; something he could laugh about to his friends later as he told how this colored barber was fool enough to think he could borrow at the bank like a white man? Barney was well enough aware that Negroes generally were considered fair game for such horseplay.

Julia was confident that the banker meant what he said. Like some wives, she believed her husband to be well-nigh faultless, and she could see nothing unusual in Kountze's proposal.

At intervals she wept and laughed hysterically, crying out that her husband was the first runaway slave ever to go into a white man's bank and borrow such a sum on his personal note. She said she doubted if his white half-brother, Claiborne, could do as much, and Louis Napoleon and his baby sister, Sadie, would grow up to be mighty proud of their papa.

Barney would not permit himself to believe it was true until he actually had the banker's signature, but he procured plans and bids for a two-story building, and the total cost of building and furnishings totalled nine thousand dollars.

When he placed everything on Kountze's desk, he was half expecting the banker to burst into a laugh and tell him to get the hell out of there, who did he think he was, a white man? But Luther Kountze was not the kind to say one thing and do another.

When he had offered to lend Barney nine thousand dollars, it was the equivalent of money in the bank. He asked him to sign a personal note, with interest at twenty-five per cent, credited his account with the money, and that completed the deal.

After being swindled by the confidence man and the claim jumpers and the lawyer, he had become understandably bitter at the white man's treatment of the colored, but now he was forced to change his mind.

White men aren't all crooks and cheats, he concluded. Black or white, human beings are pretty much the same. Regardless of race or color, the percentage of the dishonest to decent folk runs about the same.

He was thinking of what Julia had said about Claiborne. By grapevine he had learned that his white half-brother now was serving as a captain in the Confederate forces. Of course Claiborne could borrow far more than nine thousand dollars, with the plantation as security.

But what if, like Barney, his assets came to three hundred dollars less than nothing? Could he go into a bank and borrow nine thousand dollars on his personal note? Barney was certain that

121

Phoebe would be proud, could she know the esteem in which her son was held by the whites of Denver.

He soon learned that Kountze was not lending to every applicant. He rejected loan applications of several white businessmen wishing to rebuild. He refused to lend to any frequenter of Ed Chase's gambling place.

Publisher Byers was not the kind to risk his money in the Progressive. Kountze Brothers lent him six hundred dollars, but when Byers failed to pay, the bank sued him in 1868 for $3,000, and finally the suit was settled out of court.

Under the name of the People's Restaurant, Barney's new establishment opened for business on August 16, 1863, with the restaurant on the ground floor, a bar on the second, and a barber shop and hairdressing salon in the basement.

Publisher Byers even published a paragraph in the *News* about it, writing, "If you want an easy shave or your hair trimmed in approved style, Ford or his operator is the man to do it."

This was the first time Barney's name had ever appeared in a newspaper, and the proud Julia bought a scrap book at Dave Moffat's stationery store and pasted the clipping on the first page and predicted that some day the book would contain many more clippings. Although Barney merely laughed, in secret he was fully as pleased at this first appearance of his name in print.

He was grateful to Byers and went to his office and placed an advertisement in the paper, stating that he respectfully informed the public that they could get fresh oysters, lemons, and genuine Havana cigars at his place. It was necessary to freight these products seven hundred miles overland from the Missouri, and the stocking of fresh oysters and lemons was something about which to boast. Julia pasted the advertisement in her scrap book.

At the *News* office he encountered Owen J. Goldrick, the local editor and reporter, by far the most highly educated man in Denver and probably the best-dressed. In black broadcloth, boiled shirt, stovepipe hat, and kid gloves, with his muttonchop whiskers, he presented somewhat the appearance of a preacher. He was the only person Barney had ever met who could excel him in quoting the classics, and, too, he could quote in Latin and Greek. Everyone called him "the professor."

Born and educated in the north of Ireland, Goldrick, after migrating to America, found employment in Pennsylvania tutoring wealthy young James Donald Cameron, preparing him for Princeton. Subsequently Cameron became a railroad president, United States Senator, and Secretary of War.

Goldrick came west to tutor the children of a well-to-do family in the Huerfano country in southern Colorado, but, unable to cope with the loneliness, joined a train of ox-drawn freight wagons headed for Denver. Never before had residents of the settlement beheld a bullwhacker wearing stovepipe hat, white shirt, and kid gloves.

Presently he organized a day school in a dirt-floor cabin, and subsequently a Sunday School class. Parents, however, felt him to be unqualified as a Sunday School teacher because he had frequent recourse to a flask of Taos Lightning he carried in a hip pocket, so he wound up writing locals for the *News,* and the community was satisfied, since as everyone knew, whisky and newspaper writers seem to possess an affinity, one for the other.

For several years he remained single, although many a Denver belle was impressed by his elegant attire and polished manners. Occasionally he would drop in at Barney's place for a haircut, and sometimes he would write a local for the newspaper, such as:

> Mr. B. L. Ford and his polite attaches are just the gents to dispense hot and cooling aliment to one's individual wants.

Byers considered himself fortunate to acquire the services of a local editor with such a masterful command of the written word. Byers confined himself largely to the writing of editorials which, his readers felt, demanded little thought.

Barney's writing was limited to his correspondence and the preparation of advertising copy. One of these ads that Julia proudly pasted in her scrap book concluded:

> A shaving and hairdressing saloon is connected with the establishment, wherein competent artists are ever pleased to wait on customers in first-class style.

These advertisements grew larger and larger as the business prospered, and Barney's receipts soon surpassed those of the best months of his Nicaragua hotels. Exactly ninety days after the opening of his restaurant, he walked into Kountze's bank and repaid his loan, plus interest. Thereafter his credit was so good that he had no need of it. He was welcome to borrow any amount within reason, the banker told him, but business was booming and he had no occasion to seek another loan, and he kept building his account at the bank. As his law of positivities had indicated, he seemed well on the road to riches.

Meanwhile, in June of 1862 Congress virtually nullified the Dred Scott decision of the Supreme Court by approving an act prohibiting slavery in the Territories. Naturally Barney and Sanderlin were delighted, for this was welcome news for all the colored people, coming so soon after the First Territorial Legislature had accorded the black man the right to vote.

The war was proceeding none too well for the North, and the Union armies had suffered humiliating defeats. Nevertheless in September Lincoln announced that he proposed to free the slaves the following New Year day. Actually this emancipation proclamation ended slavery only in the rebel states of the South.

The following spring, by ones and twos and threes, some of the boldest of these freedmen began drifting into Denver, seeking the advantages of their new freedom. They were a sorry lot, ignorant, penniless, and well-nigh helpless, but hopeful and ambitious and expectant as they sought the opportunity about which they had dreamed all their lives.

Having been a slave himself, Barney could understand what was in the hearts of these black people, and it wrenched his feelings to note how their hopes were being dashed. Since he was prospering once more, he aided them financially, fed them, and tried to find jobs for them.

In April of 1862 Governor Gilpin had been succeeded by John Evans, a founder of Northwestern University and the man for whom Evanston, Illinois, had been named. He wore a patriarchal beard, had advocated the emancipation of the slaves, and had served as delegate to the Illinois state convention that nominated Lincoln.

Barney reasoned that he was a governor who could be counted a friend of the colored man.

The Territory's first election law, approved by Gilpin November 6, 1861, not only provided that all males of more than twenty-one could vote, but also extended the voting franchise to Indians declared citizens by treaty.

It likewise permitted any qualified elector to hold public office, and for a few weeks a mulatto had held the appointive office of assistant district attorney for Arapahoe County. He had resigned to join the rush to the Montana gold fields, and Barney had little use for him because he was ashamed of his race and sought to account for his dark skin by claiming to be part Indian — a fairly common practice among mulattoes.

In 1863 Hiram P. Bennet, the Territory's delegate to Congress, a former Free Soiler who had defeated former Governor Gilpin in the 1862 Congressional election, introduced a statehood bill for Colorado, but it never emerged from committee.

Meanwhile, in spite of the war — or perhaps because of it in case of the draft dodgers — a small but steady stream of emigrants kept trickling into Denver during the summer months, bringing more customers to Barney's prospering People's Restaurant. He failed to realize that the majority of these newcomers were from the South and were bringing about a change in public sentiment toward the Negro.

During the 1864 session of the Legislature a few Republicans joined forces with the Southern Democrats and, without public notice or newspaper publicity, adopted an amendment to the election laws barring the colored man from voting.

Into the sentence reading, "That every male person of the age of 21 years and upwards shall be deemed a qualified voter," they inserted the words, *"not being a Negro or mulatto."*

Barney learned of the passage of the amendment only after the adjournment of the Legislature, and he was dumfounded. He could scarcely believe that Governor Evans, a Lincoln supporter who had boasted of favoring emancipation, could have failed to veto such an amendment.

But when he checked the records, he discovered that the amendment had been approved March 11, 1864. It was not the first time his faith in white men had been shattered.

Since the Republicans stood for emancipation of the slaves, Barney, like all members of his race, considered himself a Republican. Immediately he consulted his friend, Byers, to learn what might be done about it. The publisher said that since the amendment now was incorporated in the election laws, nothing could be accomplished until the next session of the Legislature.

He said it would be unwise to print anything about it now, since Congress had just approved an act to enable the people of the Territory to form a state government. Byers was unable to look Barney in the eye and seemed only too eager to avoid the controversial race issue.

Barney contemplated going to Byers' competitor, Frederick J. Stanton, publisher of the *Gazette*. An ardent pro-slavery man, Stanton had charged in his editorials that Evans was a rich Chicagoan who had accepted appointment as governor of Colorado Territory as the cheapest means of gaining a seat in the United States Senate, had brought political ward-heelers from the Chicago slums, and had given them jobs in Colorado to build a machine to further his campaign for the Senate.

But Barney felt that it would be a waste of time to approach Stanton; moreover, he had worked out another equation, and it had indicated that the colored man was certain to win the right to vote once more.

Once before he had worked out just such a problem, and the answer had been correct. For two years Colorado Territory had permitted the colored man to vote, and it was not the fault of his law of positivities that subsequently the Legislature had changed the law.

XIII

When Barney pinned him down, Publisher Byers finally came out unequivocally with the statement that he could not support voting equality for Negroes because the sentiment of the Territoy was strongly opposed to it. He maintained that the situation would be different if they were all intelligent and college-educated like Barney, but it would be a crime to give the vote to these illiterate ex-slaves. What could they possibly know about the tariff or foreign policy or any of the pressing governmental problems that the voters must decide?

Barney argued that if it was reasonable to give the vote to treaty Indians who not only were unable to read or write but could not even speak or understand English, why was it not equally reasonable to give it to the colored people, who were really beginning to take an interest in questions of the day?

This argument angered Byers because he could find no answer for it, but it failed to change his position. He was opposed to equal suffrage, and that was that.

Barney was delighted when W. J. Hardin appeared in Denver. Hardin was an educated octoroon, and his skin was lighter than that of most tanned white men. He became proprietor of a billiard saloon and bowling alley.

He was a Kentuckian who had come to Denver after spending several years in Omaha, and was a gifted spell-binding orator. Barney himself possessed but limited talent for speechmaking, so he was highly pleased when Hardin appeared, even though the newcomer was given to claiming kinship to some of the outstanding white families of Kentucky.

Barney was proud of his race. What did he owe his white father or his white half-brother? Nothing! He owed everything to his black mother who had whipped ambition into him and showed him the importance of learning. He did not hate his white half-brother, but neither did he owe him anything.

As soon as the slaves were freed, Aunt Clara Brown returned to Missouri to aid her kinfolk. She brought not only her husband and children to Colorado, but thirty-four nieces and nephews and uncles and aunts and in-laws, as well.

Among the freed slaves drifting into Denver was old Lije Wentworth. Barney found him a job soliciting for the Bon Ton Hotel, and Lije would meet all the stagecoaches, ring a huge bell, ballyhoo the hotel, carry carpetbags and valises, and make himself generally useful, as Barney had done on his job at the Hemenway House.

Lije developed a sideline of finding lost children, marching up and down the dusty street ringing his bell and chanting:

> Lost child! Lost child! Done gone away from home
>   and nobody know where he gone.
> Anybody find this child, take him down to Wolfe
>   Londoner's, get five dollars.
> Here you is! Here you is!

Londoner, owner of a grocery store, later became mayor of Denver.

Old Lije was unable to read or write, but everyone loved him, especially the children. He was ignorant of the meaning of the word "tariff," and the whites held him up as an example, saying, "You want an addle-pate nigger like old Lije voting on important national questions? Well, then!"

Among the local characters was an old trapper who visited Denver periodically to sell his furs to Ceran St. Vrain and then get drunk and wind up in jail. He could neither read nor write, and was typical of many of the old mountain men.

But no one ever demanded that he be barred from voting because, like old Lije, he was illiterate. His skin was white and Lije's black. Denver numbered more white illiterates than black, but no white man would accept that as an argument.

Most of them evaded the issue with the argument that they favored a literacy test, but if asked, did they mean a literacy test for whites as well as blacks, they lost their tempers and asked, did you think they were crazy?

Barney worked unremittingly before the June election, when the voters were to choose delegates to the Constitutional Convention which was to meet July 4 to draft a constitution for the proposed new state of Colorado. He thought that perhaps he had swung a delegate or two in Denver in favor of equal suffrage, but was uncertain of the delegates from the remainder of the Territory.

Hardin and Sanderlin and a few whites worked just as hard, but despite all their efforts, the convention voted into the proposed constitution a clause limiting the vote to white males.

The defeat left Barney downhearted and disheartened. The Territorial Legislature had barred the black man from voting, but he hoped that the state constitution might override the legislative act.

The Union Party called a convention for August 2 to nominate candidates for office in the proposed new state. Many voters believed the statehood movement to be merely a scheme to elevate Governor Evans to a seat in the Senate, cheaply and easily.

After the nomination of Evans, Barney approached him seeking an equal suffrage pledge, but the candidate seemed to think it a matter better left to a vote of the people. His senatorial running mate was Henry M. Teller.

Barney set out to defeat the proposed constitution at the September election, but his influence was negligible because under the Evans administration the Territorial Legislature had barred Negroes from the polls.

The proposed constitution was snowed under by the voters, not because the suffrage clause was an issue, but because they believed it would cost the taxpayers less to support a Territorial government.

Although generally Evans was held in high repute, many voters felt that the taxpayers should not incur the additional expense of statehood merely to gratify his senatorial ambition.

Some persons accorded Barney more credit than was his due, exaggerating the facts to make it appear that he had defeated the constitution single-handed. This belief did him no harm at the time, but later when he became a candidate for office he suffered for it.

His restaurant was bringing him a satisfactory income, and he returned to his business highly pleased, confident that a major victory had been won.

As a steamboat steward and later during his Chicago barbering days, he had studied and imitated the dress of his outstanding white customers. He wore no loud silk waistcoats, no huge diamonds like those of the gambler, Ed Chase, for he was reluctant to give anyone reason to say that prosperity was going to his head. He did, however, acquire a heavy gold watch chain similar to the one he had admired so greatly on Big Thompson, but all businessmen wore such chains.

When the restaurant had paid off its debt, he had bought a cottage on Water Street — at that time no one would rent to Negro tenants — and Julia had ceased waiting on table to devote her entire time to rearing Louis Napoleon and Little Sadie.

He never doubted that they were the most attractive youngsters in Denver. Their hair was straight and Sadie's skin was the same blanched-almond shade as that of her mother.

Now slavery was an issue in Colorado no longer. The Colorado and Nevada statehood bills introduced in Congress in 1864 provided that the constitutional conventions of each must forever eliminate slavery.

In 1865 the Colorado statehood battle was resumed. This time Jerome B. Chaffee, the thirty-five-year-old Republican leader who had taken a fortune from the Bobtail Lode in Gilpin County, was to be Evans' senatorial running mate in place of Teller.

The new Constitutional Convention met August 8. After extended debate the delegates made a deal designed to sidestep the controversial suffrage issue.

To please the anti-Negro vote, the convention was to limit the franchise to whites; and to win the votes of the other faction, the question of Negro suffrage was to be submitted to the people at the same election as the state ticket and the proposed constitution.

The convention went on record against slavery but barred Negroes from voting, 32 to 9. Byers threw the support of the *News* squarely behind the anti-Negro constitution.

The publisher detested his competitor, Stanton, and frequently blasted him in editorials. He even accused the rival editor's children of stealing from the mails, so Stanton attacked him on the street and beat him unmercifully with a cane. Byers' partner and business manager, John Dailey, went hunting for Stanton with a gun, and the police were compelled to take a hand to prevent bloodshed.

This time Barney found himself facing a two-fold battle; to defeat the proposed constitution and to carry the proposal to grant his people the vote. He failed by a narrow margin to win his fight against the constitution, which was approved 3,035 to 2,870, but suffered a crushing defeat on the suffrage proposal. It was snowed under, 4,192 to 476, a margin of almost ten to one.

The people had spoken; the white people, that is. Certainly they did not wish to give the colored man the right to vote. Barney was keenly hurt to think that nine out of ten of his white customers, while pretending to be his friend, felt that he was not entitled to vote because his skin was not white. It hurt him that his friend Byers had fought against him and against his people.

Well, if the whites of Colorado hated him that much, to hell with them! He was not one to force himself on anyone. He was well off. He was not forced to remain in Colorado. He was forty-three years old and possessed enough money so he never need work again.

He determined to retire; to sell his business, return to Chicago, and take it easy for the rest of his days. Confiding nothing to Julia, he arranged with his business neighbor, Riethmann, to sell him the restaurant for $23,400 cash and to lease the building to him for $250 a month.

This was the most cash he had ever possessed, and he thought it doubtful if any runaway slave in the entire country had done so well in so short a time. With an income of $250 a month, he could live like a king in Chicago. He employed a lawyer to take charge of his Denver affairs, for he still owned a considerable amount of improved and unimproved real estate.

Julia did not approve of his plan to leave Denver and wept a little as she clipped from the *News* the reports of the restaurant sale to paste in her scrap book.

Upon reaching Chicago, he bought a pretentious home, well satisfied with himself, although still bitterly resentful of the decision of the Colorado voters.

Meanwhile Lee's army had surrendered to Grant at Appomattox Court House and the war came to an end. Lincoln had been assassinated. The Thirteenth Amendment, forever barring slavery in the United States, was ratified in December. Barney's white half-brother had returned from the war to find most of his slaves missing and the plantation operations demoralized.

Although Barney hated slavery, he could never bring himself to hate his easy-going, likable half-brother. Upon learning from a freed Carolina slave of Claiborne's predicament, he was of half a mind to make an attempt to aid him financially.

For a long time he considered the idea, but finally rejected it, although later his conscience troubled him. After all, he had never known if Claiborne ever had been aware of the mulatto slave's relationship to him. And unless Barney was mightily mistaken, Claiborne's pride would prevent him from accepting help from his former slave. Morever, he might look upon such an offer as a deliberate effort to humiliate him by emphasizing the change in their worldly conditions.

Furthermore, Barney had spent most of his capital on his Chicago home and lacked ready cash, and the income from his Denver property, while sufficient to keep him in comfort, left nothing for a loan of enough size to be of help to the luckless planter. He wondered if Phoebe would wish him to aid his white half-brother.

In November he received a letter from Wagoner who, now that the war was ended, had returned to Denver and was employed as a barber. President Andrew Johnson had appointed Alexander Cummings — founder of the New York *World* — to succeed the ambitious Evans as Territorial governor, and the new chief executive appeared to be friendly to the cause of the colored man.

The new legislature, Wagoner reported, had designated Evans and Chaffee as provisional United States Senators, to take office when and if Congress approved the constitution and granted statehood. The legislature had pledged itself, should Colorado become a state, to incorporate the substance of the anti-slavery Thirteenth Amendment in a state constitutional amendment.

The new statehood bill was to be considered by Congress shortly, but the prospect, wrote Wagoner, was discouraging now that Barney was not in Colorado to take the lead, but perhaps he wouldn't mind taking the time to help by writing letters to Senator Sumner and other influential friends of the colored man?

Somehow Wagoner's letter left Barney with a feeling of shame and guilt, as if he had abandoned his closest friends when they most needed him. They were fighting an uphill battle with no one to lead them, with no money, with nothing but determination.

And the leader whom they had trusted and relied upon, what had he done? Quit at the first setback. Abandoned the fight. What a friend Barney Ford had proved to be!

Barney Ford, the quitter, enjoying spending his money! What cared the rich Barney Ford about his people in Colorado, now that he was a capitalist in Chicago?

Barney Ford, willing enough to accept all the credit when his side was winning, but who fled like a frightened rabbit, turning his back on his own race when he was most needed! Barney Ford the welsher, Barney Ford who forgot his closest friends, Barney Ford, rich, soft and gutless!

Then and there he began to hate himself. What had happened to the Barney Ford who had risked prison a hundred times during the days of the Underground? Why wasn't he back there in the thick of the Colorado fight?

Wasn't there more to life than getting rich so one could sit back and take it easy? A hell of a fine example to his race he had turned out to be! It would break Phoebe's heart, if she knew.

He became so worked up that he sent a telegram to Wagoner — the Western Union had built into Denver by this time — offering to take the next train to Julesburg and the next stagecoach to Denver.

Then he sat down and with his pencil began to work out this problem on paper. Some time had elapsed since he had worked an equation, for one is inclined to mental laziness when he no longer is compelled to work for his livelihood.

This time his problem proved to be more formidable. Sometimes it indicated that the colored people were to win the vote, sometimes that their cause was hopeless. It marked the first time that his law of positivities had been so confused.

At length he threw down his pencil, crushed it underfoot, and asked himself what was the difference if he knew whether he were to win or lose? It was unnecessary for Wagoner and Sanderlin and Price and Hardin to know if they would win; it was enough to know that they were fighting for the right. Far better to go down fighting than to waste time speculating on victory.

Barney almost persuaded himself to board the next westbound train, but decided to await Wagoner's reply. The answering letter proved to be politely cool. Wagoner wrote that there was little that Barney could accomplish in Colorado. The whites had voted ten to one against granting the vote to Negroes, and there was no changing that.

What they really needed was someone to represent them in Washington, for that was where the decision would be made, someone acquainted with Senator Sumner and the other leaders in Congress whose influence would count.

Would Barney be interested in going to Washington to lobby against the statehood bill? They wished to put him to no expense, and had taken up a collection of fifty-four dollars and probably could raise as much more later.

Barney knew well enough the impossibility of raising ten dollars in cash among all the freedmen in Colorado, so most of that fund must have come from Sanderlin's little shop and Hardin's bowling alley and Wagoner's barber wages.

He guessed that they had discussed the matter and decided that since Barney had become so prosperous, nothing counted with him but money. And here he was, worth $23,400 and enjoying an income of $250 a month, and they thought he would do nothing for his friends or his race unless he were paid for it. They thought that he now felt that what happened to his people in Colorado was of no importance to him.

He was so angry and ashamed that he wired them that he was going to Washington at his own expense, and asked them to send him all the information he needed.

Senator Sumner remembered him and was pleased to see him. He said that they stood an even chance of beating the statehood bill, but it would demand a vast amount of work. He provided Barney with the names of several Union Republican leaders, in and out of Congress, to work on.

Back in Colorado, Hardin, taking Barney's place in leading the fight, found a powerful and unexpected ally in the new governor, Cummings, a strong supporter of race equality. He directed Hardin to prepare a petition setting forth the means by which the colored people had been deprived of the vote they had once exercised, and he promised to study it and see what could be done.

In a special message to the Legislature, he pointed out the deception that had been practiced on the petitioners when, under the Evans administration, the election laws had been amended in secret to bar Negroes and mulattoes from voting, and he demanded that the legislators "erase this odious record from the statute books."

Stanton's *Gazette* took an editorial thrust at Byers' *News* by charging that "some newspapers by their lips are advocating the claim of the colored race, yet, in reality, are in deadly hostility to them."

He termed the Evans supporters "a vile set of political hacks, nondescript refugees from the pothouses of Chicago," and said that Evans' party was "conceived in fraud, brought forth in corruption, lives in dishonesty and will die of its own depravity."

To Stanton's manner of thinking, Evans was posing in Washington as a friend of the colored man, while in Colorado he vaulted to the opposite side of the political fence. He published an editorial charging Evans with an attempt to kill two political birds with one stone by buying the opposition newspaper, the *Commonwealth*, and presenting its printing plant to Byers in return for his political support. Byers and Dailey branded the charge a dirty Copperhead lie.

Byers wrote that the governor "generally was regarded as a damned fool, and beyond doubt was foolishly demented"; he pointed out that the people had voted ten to one against granting the vote to Negroes, and claimed that the Legislature had no right to oppose the expressed will of the people.

He added that the *News* favored Negro suffrage with an educational qualification, and concluded, "Much as we may be in favor of granting the Negro his rights, we do not propose to eat, drink or sleep with one."

Meanwhile the statehood fight was coming to a head in Congress. Barney was seated in the Senate gallery when Sumner arose to read a petition opposing statehood so long as Negroes were barred from the polls. Pointing out that a basic principle of the Republican Party was race equality, he questioned that any party member could conscientiously vote to admit a state that denied equality.

The debate lingered upon population and resources, until Senator Henry S. Lane disclosed the actual issue: the word "white" in the proposed constitution.

Back in Denver Publisher Byers was demanding statehood, and became almost hysterical over the unexpected opposition developing in Congress. He charged that the colored people were "ungrateful vipers who stung the breast of the Republicans that warmed them into being," and that "the nigger blood of their leader" was responsible for this terrible ingratitude, quoting lines from Robert Burns to show him to be "a louse crawling on the curls of a queen." His tirade was directed against Hardin, not Barney.

In presenting their case Senators-elect Evans and Chaffee submitted a lengthy memorial. Stripped of surplus verbiage, it maintained that:

Except for the one word "white," everyone approves the proposed Colorado constitution.

It is untrue that the colored man is forever barred from voting, for the proposed constitution could be amended at any time.

Congress should not deny statehood to tens of thousands of stalwart whites merely because of the objections of one hundred and fifty Negroes.

Then Evans came out with a statement in the New York *Tribune* that led Barney to fear that the senator-elect had suddenly lost his mind.

First, he stated categorically that Negroes had never voted in Colorado prior to 1864. To Barney who had been so proud to cast his first ballot, it seemed impossible for Evans to make such a wild statement when the record flatly disproved it.

Second, Evans denied that as governor he had helped bar the colored man from voting and insisted that the question of Negro suffrage had not been raised during his administration.

This claim left Barney dumfounded, since the record showed that while governor, Evans had approved the amendment of March 11, 1864, specifically barring Negroes and mulattoes from voting.

Third, Evans added that the proposed constitution merely prohibited colored men from voting and holding office, and pointed out that the voters could change this provision at any time they wished. While this was true, he failed to mention the two-thirds majority necessary to amend the constitution.

Barney simply was unable to comprehend how any politician could make such a statement. Evans, it seemed to him, was not straddling the political fence, but was vaulting back and forth, on one side in Colorado and on the other in Washington.

Despite all Barney's strenuous lobbying and Senator Sumner's eloquence, the Senate approved the Colorado constitution limiting the vote to whites. In the House Congressman Washburne offered an amendment to strike the word "white" but it was rejected by a vote of 59 to 39 and the statehood bill was passed.

A bitterly disappointed Barney visited Sumner the following day, but the Senator advised him not to lose heart, for as yet the President had not signed the bill.

President Johnson had been making frequent use of the veto power, and already rumors of impeachment were being heard. He had discharged many deserving Republican officeholders, and his espousal of certain Democratic policies had alienated his own party leaders.

Colorado's senators-elect, Evans and Chaffee, were ardent Republicans of the faction opposed to Johnson's dealings with the Democrats. Politically speaking, perhaps Johnson opposed statehood for Colorado because it would have meant two additional senatorial votes against him.

Just what was in his mind when he vetoed the statehood bill no one knew, but already he was involved in so many difficulties that another veto mattered little. Barney was overjoyed, but Sumner promised him even more favorable developments. He called up a bill that had been buried in committee, a bill prohibiting any Territory — including Colorado — from denying the vote to any adult male because of race or color.

Despite the opposition of the Democrats it passed the Senate, 24 to 8, and the House, 79 to 43. Angered at Congress on general principles, President Johnson refused to sign the measure, so it became a law by constitutional limitation.

Now that the Negro could vote and his civil rights were guaranteed in Colorado Territory, Barney's battle appeared to be won. Evans had suffered a stinging defeat and had lost his opportunity to win a Senate seat. Barney wished he knew how Evans felt about the collapse of his political hopes.

Back in Denver Publisher Byers was forced to eat crow. He published a sarcastic editorial suggesting that "next thing we'll be voting for a nigger for mayor."

Thinking it over on his return journey to Chicago, Barney could see that his algebraic system had not erred. Who could blame it for becoming confused and producing answers at such variance, for the statehood vote had been uncertain, with the balloting favorable one day and unfavorable the next, which was enough to confuse even the law of positivities.

Upon reaching Chicago he found a letter advising him that the lawyer he had left in charge of his affairs had left town with another man's wife and much of his clients' cash, and Barney's business affairs were in hopeless confusion and his presence in Denver was essential immediately.

In his extremity, he sent a telegram to the only man in Denver whom he felt he could trust implicity, Luther Kountze. But the banker was touring Europe, so Barney sent C. B. Kountze his brother, power of attorney to raise money by selling fifteen parcels of his downtown real estate and to take charge of his affairs. Then he boarded the next westbound train.

XIV

Upon his return to Denver, Barney resembled a southern planter, for during his absence in Chicago and Washington he had grown a goatee. Hardin and Wagoner met him at the stagecoach station and invited him to make a speech at the Fourth of July celebration marking the victory of their cause.

Barney well knew that he was an indifferent public speaker and sought to beg off, but they told him that he had done such an excellent job in Washington that everyone would think it strange if he remained unhonored at the celebration, so he agreed.

He found Byers pretty well recovered from his defeat. He had published a congratulatory editorial asserting that the act of Congress giving the vote to the Negroes was a simple act of justice, and he "extended the hand of fellowship and welcomed them to all the proud majesty of independent citizenship" and expressed the hope that now everyone would unite against the demoralizing hands of Copperheadism and secession.

The editorial contained so many flowery phrases that Barney assumed that Goldrick had written it. The *News* certainly had turned a political somersault.

He found his business affairs in disorder, but after straightening them out, found himself far from being down to his last dollar. Riethmann continued to pay him $250 a month rent for the restaurant building. He sold his Chicago home to raise ready cash, borrowed additional funds from the bank, and arranged to construct a new building at Blake and G streets. Goldrick noted it in the *News* and Julia pasted the item in her scrap book.

During the war the federal government enacted its first income tax law, and annually all incomes of more than $3,000 a year were published in the newspapers. Barney's 1864 income, reported in 1865, was $4,673; the fourteenth largest in Denver. It exceeded the incomes reported by Chase and Heatley, the gamblers; of A. B. Daniels, merchant and banker; of Walter C. Cheesman and of Riethmann, buyer of Barney's restaurant.

It was considerably below the incomes of Luther and Charles B. Kountze, the bankers, and slightly less than the incomes of Byers and his partner, Dailey.

Denver was proud of that income tax report, which showed that the town could boast of 623 taxable persons, 185 gold watches, 116 carriages, and twenty-six pianofortes.

Barney's new restaurant did not open for business until the summer of 1866, but in spite of his reverses of the preceding year he reported a larger income for 1865, totalling $4,751. It exceeded the income of Dave Moffat, who was to become one of the West's wealthiest men.

While Barney had been in Chicago, the Commissioner of the Land Office, Washington, had ruled that Negroes possessed the same rights as whites in pre-empting land and taking up homesteads. Barney could not repress a smile at this, for he had become owner by pre-emption of his claims on the Bowman Lode, which had been jumped by the whites because it was illegal, and now he thought he might bring suit for their restoration, but upon investigation discovered that they were worthless.

When he opened his new restaurant, he took an advertisement to the *News* office, wondering if Byers would be angry at him because of the defeat of the statehood bill; but the publisher, who looked like General Grant now that his beard was grown, was unaware of his Washington lobbying activities and believed that he had been in Chicago during his absence from Denver. So Barney assumed an air of innocence and inquired about what had happened to the statehood bill.

Byers admitted that he was unable to understand it; everything had been arranged for the passage of the bill and its proponents had been confident that the President would sign it, but at the last moment unexpected opposition had developed. He suspected some sinister influence at work behind the scenes in Washington, but was unable to put his finger on it. He asserted that the failure to gain statehood had set back the progress of Colorado by ten years.

Repressing a smile, Barney asked if Byers ever considered that perhaps the statehood movement failed because it was unjust to the colored man? He could not refrain from quoting, "Thrice is he armed who has his quarrel just."

Byers wanted to argue the point and restated his position in favor of a literacy test, but when Barney agreed that he could support it if it applied to whites as well as blacks, the disgusted Byers said that he had always believed Barney had more sense, but now he doubted it.

Barney did not boast of his accomplishment in Washington, but when the colored people staged the Fourth of July celebration in the vacant lot opposite the Planters House, Hardin delivered an oration praising him for the service he had rendered his race and expressing their deepest gratitude, until the embarrassed Barney wished the platform would open and swallow him.

Goldrick was present to report the celebration for his newspaper; consequently, the whole story got back to Byers, and the following day when they met on Blake Street he grinned sheepishly and said that he never dreamed Barney had it in him to defeat Evans and the *News* combined, but let's let bygones be bygones because we're all good Republicans and must join forces to whip the Democrats at the next election.

Now that Negroes could vote, they possessed something of importance to the politicians, and although as yet the colored vote was small, even counting all of Aunt Clara Brown's kinfolk, Byers and the other Republican leaders were determined that it should not drop into the laps of the Democrats, and so was Barney.

So many whites shared Byers' view concerning an educational test — or so they said — that Barney could not dismiss it lightly. Because he had struggled so long and so diligently to "get learning," he could readily understand this argument and did not attribute it to prejudice alone.

The freed slaves that were drifting west were pitifully ignorant, for the Black Laws had made it virtually impossible to be otherwise. Where lay the difference between these pitiable, helpless freedmen and Barney himself, who was well off in spite of his recent losses, and so respected by the whites that he could borrow thousands on his personal note?

Black Phoebe had placed her finger on it; it was learning. If these colored men ever were to be recognized as equals they, too, must acquire learning.

So, with Wagoner, Hardin, and Sanderlin, Barney established Colorados' first adult education classes, to teach his people reading, writing, arithmetic, and the basic principles of government. The classes were held in Wagoner's home, adjoining the home of David Moffat, the stationer, who was beginning to engage in banking. Wagoner taught reading and writing and Barney conducted classes on the subject of government.

Since most of these ex-slaves had come from the plantations of the South, their experience was limited largely to farming, so Barney felt that their future lay in the farms of this new western country, especially since they now could take up homesteads legally.

But farming in the arid West is utterly unlike farming in the cotton country, and the colored families nearly all failed at dryland farming and drifted back to Denver to work at common labor or as unskilled workers in the service trades. Having lived their lives as slaves, they lacked initiative and looked to someone else to make their decisions and do their thinking.

Most of them stood no chance of getting ahead until the next generation came along and acquired schooling. Even so, not one would have exchanged his freedom for the security he had known as a slave.

Deeply religious, most of these Negroes had been inclined to accept slavery as the will of the Lord. As soon as they could begin to read sentences, they would start on the Bible, and poor, simple-minded old Lije Wentworth became thoroughly confused, so that he walked home from class one evening and hung over Barney's picket fence asking questions.

Foremost was that same old question that had puzzled Barney: that statement about man being created in the image of God. No white man had ever doubted that God is white. Barney's inquiries had failed to disclose one white man who believed God to be a Negro.

142

He was unable to give old Lije a satisfactory answer, but it set him to thinking, why could not his law of positivities produce the answer? Up to this time he had used his algebraic system on such simple problems as whether he would get rich or whether there would be war. But why wouldn't it prove equally effective on more complex problems, like this?

But finding out about God proved to be vastly more complicated, something that couldn't be worked out in ten or fifteen minutes. To begin with, he wrote down sixteen factors, of which fourteen were unknown. However, since in itself his system was designed to calculate unknowns, this should be no insurmountable difficulty. The problem was not impossible, and if he continued to work on it with sufficient diligence, he felt that he was certain to arrive at the correct answer.

In January of 1867 the Territorial Legislature passed a law barring Negroes from jury service, but Governor Cummings vetoed it.

Publisher Byers complained that this was merely a political scheme to thwart the statehood movement and claimed that an act of the first Territorial legislature had barred the black man from jury service from the beginning. What he failed to explain was: if it were true that the colored man already was barred, why was it necessary to pass another identical act?

At each session of Congress Colorado was introducing a new statehood bill. By this time the politicians produced a shrewd scheme to mislead the public, but it failed to deceive Barney.

This time they had omitted the word "white" that had defeated the last statehood movement, so on the face of it the bill seemed fair enough, but buried in the legal terminology was a dangerous "joker." It provided that all Territorial laws in force when the new state was admitted would continue in effect — and quite naturally this included the law amended under the Evans administration, specifically barring Negroes and mulattoes from voting.

Both houses of Congress passed the bill with little debate, but it failed to deceive President Johnson. His veto message called attention to the "sleeper" and also the scheme to provide all-white juries. An attempt was made to pass it over his veto, but sufficient votes were lacking in the Senate.

The reason Johnson was not deluded was because Senator Sumner had called his attention to the provision, and the reason Sumner detected it was because Barney had written him a letter explaining it.

According to one story making the rounds, the reason Johnson had vetoed the bill was to punish Evans and Chaffee for their refusal to pledge him their support when and if they were seated in the Senate.

He failed of impeachment in 1868 by the margin of one vote in the Senate. This raised a question, what would have been the result had Colorado become a state in 1866 and Evans and Chaffee had taken their seats in the Senate?

From the stand they had taken against Johnson, everyone assumed that they would have voted for impeachment, their two votes would have turned the balance, and Johnson would have lost by the margin of one vote.

This assumption led to another question. Had Barney not fought the statehood movement, perhaps Evans and Chaffee would have been elected, Johnson would have been impeached, and the history of the United States would have been changed.

Consequently some Coloradans began to call Barney a president-maker because they were convinced that his influence had turned the tide and kept Johnson in office.

The preceding year, when Barney had been lobbying in Washington, he learned that Byers' wife was Senator Sumner's niece, and it gave rise to another idea. Perhaps the Senator could work through his kinswoman to change the opposition of the publisher. However, he never learned precisely what toned down Byers' fiery anti-nigger editorials.

Whatever the reason, Byers wrote a surprisingly meek editorial on the veto of the statehood bill, reflecting that "to invest with the elective franchise the few colored citizens of Colorado cannot result in injury to any."

Barney was amused and pleased at Byers' change of policy and the elimination of the word "nigger" from his editorials. He himself had never given ground in his stand on race equality, and all the concessions had been made by the publisher.

144

Barney wished he knew if Byers' change of heart reflected the views of the political leaders. Evans' influence had been dwindling, and now Chaffee was becoming recognized as the helmsman of the Republican Party in the Territory.

The colored people organized a jubilee at Turnverein Hall on April 3 to celebrate their franchise victory, inviting Louis H. and Fred Douglass, Jr., sons of Frederick Douglass, to come to Denver to address the meeting.

The *News* carried a lengthy account of the meeting, deploring the manner in which the Negroes had been "wronged and downtrodden for generations." Perhaps it was intended to enlist the colored voters in the Republican ranks, but in any event the Republicans would have won.

In July Barney was chosen delegate to the Republican county convention and became the father of another daughter, Frances, called Frankie for short.

Ever since his return from Chicago, his business had been prospering, which was remarkable because Denver was in the doldrums. Since the collapse of the Pikes Peak gold boom, there had been little to keep the community alive.

The Board of Trade and virtually everyone else was seeking to promote the construction of a railroad from the east but was achieving scant results. The continental divide west of the town was like an enormous wall, and to detour about it the railroads would be forced to build south through New Mexico or north through Dakota Territory, a portion of which was soon to become Wyoming.

The Union Pacific had been built as far west as Julesburg in the northeast corner of the Territory, but instead of following the South Platte southwest to Denver, it followed a route to the northwest, and Denver residents despairingly realized that their community was to be by-passed.

A little settlement of shacks and tents known as Cheyenne was springing up some hundred miles north of Denver. Many feared that Denver was to become a ghost town like the little mining towns after their booms burst. Dave Moffat, one of the community's most competent businessmen, now a banker, was preparing to open a branch of the First National Bank at Cheyenne under the name of Rogers & Co. He still retained faith in Denver, but he was playing it safe.

In their own way Gamblers Ed Chase and Hub Heatley were fully as capable, too intelligent to back a losing game too long. They opened a branch at Cheyenne in a tent.

Barney's tenant and former business neighbor, Riethmann, established a bakery at Cheyenne. Barney discussed the situation with Julia, worked out an equation, and placed an advertisement in the *News* offering his restaurant for sale.

Entering into partnership with a grocer, John T. Durkee, he joined the rush to the new boom town and built a 22 x 60-foot adobe and concrete restaurant building, to be in readiness when the Union Pacific built into Cheyenne.

On September 24 the Cheyenne *Leader* published a notice about the new restaurant and Barney clipped it and mailed it to Julia, who had remained in Denver. When the first train rolled in, the restaurant was open for business, and during the next twenty-four hours it took in $1,150.

Business continued to boom, and presently Barney built a frame addition and opened a hotel. The *Leader* kept printing so many articles about the Ford place that Barney subscribed to the newspaper for Julia so she could make her own clippings for the growing scrap book.

In November a party of newspaper writers visited Cheyenne. It included a Frenchman, Louis Laurient Simonin, correspondent of a Paris journal. Later someone procured a copy of the Paris publication and translated his report:

> *Allons,* pioneers of the West, another step forward, another step with the sun!
>
> How rough and crude in appearance they are, all these men of the Far West, with their long hair, their felt hats with the broad brims, their ill-kept beards, their clothing of nondescript color, their great leather boots in which their pantaloons are engulfed!
>
> But what virile characters; proud, fearless! What dignity, what patience! No one complains here. If things are not better, it is because they cannot be, and no one finds anything therein to blame.

Here is the Ford restaurant, the "Vefour" of the place. They do all the business you could wish, up to $1,000 a day. Just calculate it. Meals are a dollar. They serve three meals every day, and each time 2-300 people are seated at differnt tabls. I do not mention profits of the bar, the extras, etc. There are other restaurants in Cheyenne, but Ford leads them all.

Barney learned later that "Vefour" was a leading Paris restaurant. Julia was immensely proud because he had become so famous that even the Paris newspapers publicized him.

Most of the population of Julesburg moved into Cheyenne with the Union Pacific — gamblers, fancy ladies, bad men, and holy terrors. They were lavish spenders and almost overnight inflated the population to six thousand, and for a few months Barney enjoyed a capacity business. It was too good to last, and when the railroad moved west, the boomers moved on, also.

As business declined in Cheyenne, Barney reopened his Denver restaurant under Wagoner's management and kept shuttling between the towns by stagecoach.

In March of 1868, while he was in Denver and his partner was in charge at Cheyenne, two guests of the Ford House quarreled and A. G. Burtis shot H. W. Dodge. Barney blamed his partner for catering to the wrong class of customers and bought him out for $10,000.

In later years residents of Cheyenne liked to tell the story that Barney chartered a special train to take all his friends to Baltimore for a wild party costing a small fortune. The story had but a slight basis of fact.

He specialized on oysters because they were seldom found in frontier restaurants, and on this occasion found it necessary to go to Baltimore to arrange a new contract with his supplier. When he sought to buy a ticket, the agent took note of the color of his skin and informed him that everything was sold out far in advance.

The only means he could obtain accommodations was by chartering a special car. Since he was paying for an entire car, he took Julia and the children and Wagoner and several of his closest friends with him. It was far from being a millionaire's wild party, but by the time the story passed from mouth to mouth the private car was a special train spilling over with champagne and caviar.

On the zero-cold night of January 12, 1870, while Barney was in Baltimore, the bartender at the Eagle saloon permitted the stove to become overheated, starting a fire that destroyed most of Cheyenne's business district. It was a repetition of the Denver fire of 1863.

The employees pitched the hotel and restaurant furniture into the street, but their efforts were wasted; because of the high wind, everything but the silverware was consumed by the flames.

Upon his return, Barney found Cheyenne's business district wiped out, and he was some $30,000 poorer than when he had departed for Baltimore. He sat down to work out another equation.

Under Wagoner's management, his Denver restaurant had been doing only passably well, for Wagoner's wife and one daughter had died in an epidemic and he was taking little interest in the business.

Economic conditions had been on the upturn in Denver. Although the Union Pacific had by-passed the town, it seemed reasonably certain that a spur line would be built in from Cheyenne, bringing with it a measure of prosperity.

Everyone was contributing to a fund to help finance the railroad deal. Barney and Harry Rogers, head of Moffat's Cheyenne branch bank, sent $3,700 to the railroad fund.

There were rumors afloat that other railroads were planning to build into Denver from the east. The answer to Barney's equation indicated that he should return to Denver immediately.

Closing out his Cheyenne business at a loss, he bought a place at 42 Blake Street, across the street from the spot where Denver's new railroad station was to be built. It was a combination hotel and restaurant called the Ford House and People's Restaurant.

The first train from Cheyenne pulled in on the Denver Pacific on June 15, 1870, and two months later the Kansas Pacific built in from the east.

Within another month the Colorado Central was built from Denver to Golden, and real estate values skyrocketed. Within a few months Barney was offered three times what he had paid for his new hotel property.

The following January, the Denver & Boulder Valley railroad tapped the coal fields at Erie, signalized by a huge celebration on a special train, with Dave Moffat himself and railroad presidents and politicians participating. Barney provided champagne so everyone would have a gay time.

Meanwhile still another railroad was being built, the Denver & Rio Grande, and by October it linked Colorado Springs and Denver and was pushing on south and west.

The railroad boom surpassed even the early Pikes Peak gold stampede. Barney's algebra indicated that he would do well to invest in real estate, and his investments paid handsomely, enabling him to enter the banking business with some of the leading capitalists of the Territory.

The runaway slave had come a long way.

XV

Participating with Barney in the organization of the new bank were the following trustees:

His friend and erstwhile political enemy, Byers of the *News*; Jerome B. Chaffee, leader of the Republican Party, who had been defeated by Barney in the statehood fight; Edward M. McCook, Civil War general and former resident minister to the Sandwich Islands, appointed governor of Colorado Territory by Grant in 1869; Daniel Witter, brother-in-law of Vice-president Schuyler Colfax, chairman of the Republican Territorial Central Committee and candidate for governor in 1864.

Among the incorporators who were not trustees was former governor Evans, who might have been a United States Senator except for the statehood struggle. The name of the institution was the Dime Savings Bank and it was capitalized at $100,000.

Julia was jubilant as she pasted the newspaper clipping in her scrap book. She surmised that her husband doubtless was the first ex-slave ever to become a bank trustee with such a group of wealthy and outstanding white leaders.

Barney felt that Phoebe would be pleased to know how well her son was getting on in the world, but his success did not lead him to forget his people.

Sam Patterson had organized a farm colony in Huerfano County for freed slaves from Georgia. The party of colonists had made their way across the plains in a collection of rickety mule-drawn wagons, only to wind up in the river bottoms below Denver, half-starved and penniless.

Barney took the party under his wing, supplying them with

150

food from his restaurant, paying for wagon repairs, stocking them with supplies, and getting them on their feet again. Byers made note of it in the *News*.

One of the colored boys brought him word of Barney's white half-brother, who had lost the plantation in the post-war collapse and was working as a cotton buyer for a Charleston firm and was finding solace in the bottle. Barney sincerely regretted to learn of Claiborne's misfortune.

He had never forgot his mother's prediction that if he only "got learning in his head," some day he could stand on the gallery of his own house and the whites would shake him by the hand and call him *Mister*. Already many — especially the politicians — were shaking his hand and calling him Mister Ford, but he lacked a gallery.

So he and Julia began planning to build one of the outstanding homes in Denver. They bought lots in the choicest residence district at E and Champa streets and consulted an architect, who convinced them that the plantation style of architecture was unsuited to Denver climate.

Their new home was to be a two-story brick with eleven-foot ceilings and a sixty-four-foot gallery — the architect called it a veranda — across the front and another on the side, both trimmed with latticework. It was to have the latest type windows operating with cords and weights, and a genuine cast iron fireplace mantel in the front parlor.

One of the modern innovations was a well in the back yard with a force pump capable of pouring water on the roof in case of fire.

Like all the new residences of the well-to-do, it included a bathing room with a sheet metal tub. Barney made no effort to save on the coal shed and stables, but built them of brick, like the house.

When the home was finished, Byers published a lengthy article describing it from the brick cellar to the tin roof cornice and the Gothic style picket fence. Julia not only pasted the account in her scrap book, but sent clippings to all her friends and kinfolk in Chicago.

First to call on the Fords at their new home were the politicians, and a few even brought their wives. Barney always welcomed them on the veranda, just as Claiborne had done on the old plantation, and served juleps to those who wished them. He seldom used liquor, but kept a supply in the cellar for hospitality's sake.

He could not but regret that Claiborne no longer possessed a gallery of his own. Barney was forty-nine years old now, so his brother was past sixty.

Was Claiborne's hair grey? Did he still stand ramrod-erect? Had poverty brought him shabbiness?

Barney could scarce imagine the once-handsome Claiborne a broken old man; could not picture the former master of so many slaves working for someone else. His misfortune must have proved a bitter pill.

Back in Chicago in 1865 when he had retired on his fortune of $23,400, his conscience had troubled him over his failure to aid his white half-brother. At that time a loan would have pinched him, but now he was reported to be worth a quarter of a million and could easily spare a few thousand. He worked out another equation, but because of one known factor, Claiborne's pride, it produced no satisfactory answer.

Nevertheless he consulted his lawyer and arranged for the attorney to send his own check to a lawyer at Charleston, with instructions to offer the money to Claiborne as an anonymous gift, if possible, but if not, as a loan.

Thus he believed he had eliminated the factor of Claiborne's pride. If Claiborne were not aware that the money came from his Negro half-brother and former slave, perhaps he would accept it. Barney still wondered if the white kinsman realized that the mulatto slave boy sold by Old Missy's orders was his own half-brother.

A month later the money was returned with a letter from the Charleston lawyer. With all the courtesy of a gentleman of the Old South, Claiborne wished to express his heartfelt gratitude to his unknown friend and to advise him that he, Claiborne, was fully capable of caring for himself.

Actually, wrote the Charleston lawyer, Claiborne was occupying a furnished room in the home of an old-time family friend, but in spite of some trouble with rheumatism, was regularly employed. His wife had died some years previously and there were no children.

"He'p him, Lord," Phoebe had prayed for her Barney back in the slave days. "I tried to he'p him, but I don't know how."

Well, Barney had tried to help his white half-brother, but he simply didn't know how. He sent word to the Charleston lawyer to keep an eye on Claiborne and if he lost his job or was taken ill, to keep him advised.

Always he had hated slavery because of the oppression of the slave. Now he was beginning to see how it sapped the enterprise and energy of the slaveholder. Claiborne had been likable, intelligent, and, as a planter using wageless slave labor, reasonably capable.

In the slave days he had never needed to work, so when the time came that he was forced to make his way in a highly competitive environment, he simply did not have it in him. Through his youth and early manhood he had never been forced to develop muscle, so when he needed them most those muscles, mental as well as physical, were soft and flabby.

Barney's advancement had resulted largely from the strenuous life he had been compelled to live, the battles he had fought, and the obstacles he had overcome, but each defeat had taught him something.

He had been forced to fight for every dollar that he owned and for every political gain for his people, and nothing had ever been handed to him on a silver platter. No one ever built muscle by lifting cream puffs from a silver platter.

In 1868, two years after Congress passed the Civil Rights Act, the Fourteenth Amendment was ratified. It provided that everyone born or naturalized in the United States is a citizen.

Once more Colorado was clamoring for statehood. In the spring of 1868 it was reasonably certain that the Republicans would nominate General Ulysses S. Grant for president, and he was receptive. When he visited Denver with Generals William Tecumseh Sherman and Phil Sheridan, it was generally assumed that his motive was political.

The three generals were taken by stagecoach to the Central

City mining district and upon their return were guests of honor at a reception at Masonic Hall. At midnight the party adjourned to Barney's hotel for a banquet and political discussions.

There were no speeches, but the hospitality loosened Sherman's tongue and he talked so much that the local political leaders could scarce get a word in edgewise, but Barney managed to exchange a few productive sentences with Grant.

In January the Territorial Legislature had adopted a resolution petitioning Congress for statehood. This time the Colorado politicians were shrewder than they had been before their bitter experience with that word "white."

As introduced February 12, the statehood resolution provided, partly due to Barney's efforts, for equal suffrage for the colored man. Since the Colorado voters had rejected equal suffrage by a vote of ten to one, the abrupt about-face of the statehood resolution might have appeared to be tempting disaster.

At last the political leaders, however, had accepted the logic of Barney's argument that the expressed will of the people of the Territory meant nothing. What counted were the votes of a Republican abolitionist Congress. It was in Washington, through Sumner and others, where Barney could really make his influence felt. By now the Colorado leaders were well aware of the pressure he was capable of bringing.

Up to this time he had gone to Evans and Chaffee and Byers and begged them to support equality at the polls, but they had always made the excuse that the people had spoken and they dared not oppose the will of the voters.

But now these leaders were coming to him and asking his support in return for their pledge to advocate equality in the proposed constitution. They needed him on their side if they expected the statehood movement to succeed.

Barney had always been prepared to work for statehood as long as the constitution guaranteed his people equal rights. So the deal was made, and now he threw all his resources into the fight on behalf of statehood.

At the banquet at the Ford House, Barney was among the statehood advocates. General Grant sat and smiled behind his cigar and said nothing, but everyone knew that a Union general could never oppose voting equality.

Shortly after the Republicans nominated Grant, Evans and Chaffee "resigned" from the senatorial seats they had sought but never held, their announced reason being "to eliminate personal considerations from the statehood fight."

Many persons were convinced that Barney had forced the Evans resignation because Negroes had been denied the vote during his administration, but this was sheer guesswork, although Barney had opposed him politically even though now they were on the board of the same bank.

The statehood resolution died in committee, but it made little difference, so far as Barney's struggle for the rights of his people was concerned, for in March of 1870 the Fifteenth Amendment was ratified. The third of the reconstruction amendments, it provided that the right to vote could not be denied on account of race or color.

Barney heaved a vast sigh of relief, for he believed that now the colored man's voting rights were protected forever.

He was one of the principal speakers at a meeting at the Denver Theater, called to celebrate ratification of the amendment. He was far less eloquent than Wagoner's son, Henry, Jr., a promising young man who seemed destined some day to become a leader of his race. The account in the *News* described him as "one of the city's up-and-coming young men."

Young Henry went to Washington, D.C., to study law, and after gaining his L.L.B. degree, was admitted to the bar by the Supreme Court of the District of Columbia, entered government service with the Pension Bureau, and was named recorder of claims.

Shortly he was appointed United States consul at Lyons, France, and appeared to be carving out one of the most brilliant careers of any young man of his race, but suddenly he was taken ill and died.

Coming so soon after the deaths of his wife and daughter, young Henry's death was a stunning blow to Wagoner. It saddened Barney and led him to some serious thinking about that matter of man being made in the image of God.

Did Henry's death indicate that God was white and cared nothing for the black man? Why had He permitted such a promising young fellow to be cut down just as he was getting started on such a brilliant career?

The greatest need of the Negroes was education and leadership, and here was one young man who might have become an outstanding national leader. So far as higher education was concerned, he had been one in a million and might have become another Frederick Douglass.

What had been in God's mind when He let Henry die? Were the cards stacked against the black man up above, as they were here on earth? As yet, it was something that Barney was unable to calculate by means of algebra, although he felt that he was making progress in ciphering his way into the Unknown.

He could not avoid contrasting young Wagoner's case with that of Jim Hill, who killed a white man during a quarrel at Capitol Hall and was condemned to die.

Barney and Wagoner felt certain that, had Jim's skin been white, the result of the trial would have been different; so, since he was without funds to hire lawyers, they raised a defense fund to appeal his conviction. The Supreme Court reversed the case, and at his second trial Jim was sentenced to life imprisonment.

Now, Barney kept asking himself, why did God turn His back on brilliant young Henry Wagoner, who might have accomplished so much for his people, at the very time He was saving Jim Hill from the gallows?

By 1872 the political pot was beginning to boil once more, and Wagoner wrote a letter to the *News* criticizing the Republicans for their failure to accord more recognition to the colored people.

Immediately Barney was named a member of the Republican County Central Committee, of which Publisher Byers was chairman. Two years earlier Barney had organized the Colored Republican Club and generally was regarded as the leader of his race in Denver.

He was not sufficiently naïve as to believe that the political leaders were acting from sheer nobility of nature and kindness of heart.

Before the coming of the railroads, Denver's Negro population had been relatively small and its vote unimportant. Political leaders of both parties mistakenly believed that this bloc would always vote Republican.

The railroads brought in huge crews of track laborers, for the most part freed slaves from Georgia. Generally speaking, the whites refused to rent to them and they were too poor to buy, so the railroads established a segregated district of their own at the foot of Twenty-second Street, commonly known as the Deep South. Later the Negro population shifted to the Five Points district.

Denver's Deep South represented a considerable number of votes, and doubtless this was the reason that the political bosses wanted Barney on the Central Committee. Wagoner, Hardin, and Sanderlin were named delegates to the Republican County Convention in August.

When the Republican Club was organized, Barney was elected vice-president and was officially recognized as the leader of his people.

Shortly after opening his hotel and restaurant opposite the railroad station, he established a second restaurant on Blake Street, but felt his operations to be cramped so, in August of 1872, he sold the Blake Street place and bought the four-story brick Sargent Hotel, renaming it Ford's Hotel, and then sold his remaining restaurant.

For years Negroes had been excluded from jury service, but in November Barney was named a member of the United States grand jury, the first of his race to serve on such a body in Colorado. Julia pasted the clipping in her scrap book.

Ford's Hotel was the meeting place of the board of county commissioners. Among them was A. G. Chever, real estate dealer who used crutches because of crippling rheumatism. Barney told him that in Nicaragua he had learned how to treat rheumatism with massage, and if agreeable to Chever, he would like to demonstrate.

As it cost nothing, Chever agreed, and after Barney massaged him he discarded his crutches and walked from the hotel, apparently cured. Reporting the incident in its news columns, the *News* termed it a miracle, jokingly noting that Barney "didn't plan to quit keeping hotel in favor of doctoring, just yet."

By this time the report that Barney was worth a quarter of a million was not in the least exaggerated, and he was planning to build a hotel of which Denver could well be proud. He bought lots at the corner of Sixteenth and Blake streets and by August had built a four-story brick structure, more aristocratic than the American House diagonally opposite, although not quite so large. He called it the Inter-Ocean, and Ed Chase fancied the name so much that he adopted it, using it for his new gambling establishment on Curtis Street.

All the newspapers published lengthy articles about Denver's grand new Inter-Ocean Hotel, proclaiming it an ornament to the city and describing Barney as a public-spirited citizen. The *News* pointed out that it possessed all the most modern attractions: bathing rooms for ladies and gents, gas lights, and a patent annunciator with wires leading from every room.

Barney was rightfully proud of the Inter-Ocean, with its bronze chandeliers, grand piano, and huge plush ottoman in the parlor, and shutters that folded inside. The chairs were of black walnut and russet leather, the dove-color Brussels carpet on the main floor was ornamented with a brown oak leaf design, and the foyer boasted an eleven-foot diamond-dust pier glass.

The room furniture was trimmed with crinoline and lambrequins adorned the windows. The Inter-Ocean cost $53,000, but in 1874 Barney sold it for $75,000 to Benjamin O. Cutter, who had just come into a fortune through the sale of the Caribou mine. Barney continued to operate Ford's Hotel, the former Sargent's House.

In August of 1873 the Republican County Central Committee met at Ford's Hotel and Barney was named a delegate to the county convention. He had been urging party leaders to include a Negro on the Republican ticket, pointing out that the colored vote no longer could be ignored.

The other members of the committee believed Barney himself to be the logical candidate, since he was the recognized leader of his race, but he told them that he was uninterested in any political office.

He urged them to support Wagoner for a seat in the lower house of the Legislature, but they doubted if Wagoner was widely known among the white voters. Sanderlin, who had invested in real estate before the railroad boom and was prospering, was rejected because he had taken little interest in working for the party.

That brought them to Hardin, the spellbinding orator, who, although a comparative newcomer, seemed the logical choice until the *News* published an anonymous letter charging him to be a confessed draft dodger who had been discharged from his job at the government mint and assay office for incompetency. The letter asked if it were not true that he recently had married a white milliner of Denver, although still having a wife in Kentucky.

Then the Kansas City police asked that Hardin be held on a charge of adultery, his Kentucky wife came to Denver and confronted him in jail, and the scandal forced him to leave the city. With his white wife, he went to Nevada and later moved to Wyoming.

The scandal was a blow to Barney, since Hardin had become identified in the public mind as one of the leaders of his race.

Meanwhile, in southern Colorado "Judge" Guilford Courthouse Budd, a Pueblo barber and one of the town's earliest settlers, had announced himself a candidate for the nomination as delegate to Congress. Born a slave, he had been named for the place of his birth, Guilford Courthouse, Virginia.

The opposing Republican candidate was Henry P. H. Bromwell, a former Illinois Congressman. According to rumor, Bromwell promised to support "Judge" Budd for appointment as minister to Haiti on condition he quit the race.

Whatever the reason, Budd withdrew, so the ticket was left without a Negro candidate. As it turned out, Bromwell was defeated by Thomas M. Patterson, a Democrat.

The party leaders renewed their pressure on Barney, and finally he agreed to become a candidate for the Territorial Legislature. Byers, who had dropped the word "nigger" in his editorials, endorsed him along with the remainder of the ticket. He was the first of his race to become a candidate at the polls for a Territorial office in Colorado.

Among the reasons for his hesitation was his consciousness that he was an indifferent orator. His doubts were justified, for his speech was so precise that the white audience thought him to be "putting on airs."

He took part in all the rallies and worked unceasingly for the ticket. Oddly enough, his Democratic opponent was an uneducated white man from the South whose accent was as broad as any Negro's. Hearing them speak, one might believe that Barney was the white man and the other, the black. The *News* said people voted for Barney because his speech was pure.

Although Colorado had always gone Republican, the people had rejected Negro suffrage ten to one. They had believed in the emancipation of the slaves, but still they would have denied the Negro the right to vote or to hold public office.

The Democrat strength lay in Denver and southern Colorado, but the Republicans could expect heavy majorities elsewhere in the Territory. As a candidate in the normally Democratic Denver district, Barney faced an uphill fight.

Up to this time none but the party leaders knew how much influence he had wielded in Washington during the statehood controversies, but now that he had become a candidate, the opposition branded him as the colored man who had blocked statehood, delaying Colorado's progress for years.

A substantial segment of the population was resentful because the Fifteenth Amendment had imposed equal racial suffrage upon them against their will. As the only Negro candidate on either ticket, Barney was the target for the animosity of these dissidents, and on September 11, when the returns were all in, most of the Republican ticket had been elected, but Barney was defeated by 736 votes.

His prosperity had aroused strong feeling against him. Was it right that a nigger should make so much money when so many whites were practically starving?

Barney had earned every dollar he possessed, earned them in spite of obstacles and prejudices no white man was called upon to face. He discovered that it was all very well and quite admirable

160

for a man to achieve financial success, so long as his skin was the right color.

In December President Grant urged Congress once more to consider granting Colorado statehood status. Promptly Delegate Chaffee introduced a new bill for an enabling act.

The fear that Colorado, with less than 100,000 population, would cast as many votes in the Senate as populous New York or Pennsylvania was voiced by many eastern newspapers. One described the people of the Territory as "roving, unsettled adventurers living in a state of semi-barbarism."

Barney was working on behalf of the statehood bill, although it meant only that Congress would consider another proposed constitution. The bill passed the House easily but action in the Senate was delayed until February, 1875. It slipped through during the last hour of the session and was signed by President Grant on March 3.

He appointed John L. Routt governor of the Territory and Routt issued a call for a constitutional convention to be held the following December.

Although presumably Barney had no occasion to be disturbed, for the Fifteenth Amendment provided that no one could be denied the vote on account of race or color and he no longer needed fear the inclusion of that word "white," still he was troubled, for he was aware of rumors that the Democrats were planning to bar the Negro voters by means of an educational test and a poll tax.

He found himself fighting for two objectives. First, he must make certain that the Republicans elected sufficient delegates to control the convention, and so forestall any attempt to include another "sleeper" in the constitution.

At the same time, he must work for the election of a Republican legislature so that, when and if Colorado finally became a state, no loaded election laws could be passed.

Ed Chase would not have risked a dollar on his chances of winning both objectives, and Barney himself was doubtful until he sat down and worked out another equation.

XVI

The Republicans elected twenty-four of the thirty-nine convention delegates, insuring a constitution free of race discrimination. The delegates debated for eighty-five days but, as Barney expected, produced a constitution providing for equality at the polls.

Only a few years had passed since the people had voted ten to one against equal suffrage, and presumably many of the delegates looked askance at the equality clause, but they were well aware that there was no chance of attaining statehood without it — not after adoption of the Fifteenth Amendment; not with a Republican Congress that would stand for no discrimination.

Perhaps these delegates had responded to the whispering campaign; "Sure, let's vote this way because we must, but just wait until the first State Legislature is elected, and then we can slip a literacy test into the election laws."

When the constitution was submitted to the voters it was ratified, 15,443 to 4,062. Three days later, on the Fourth of July, Colorado celebrated in advance the winning of statehood, for now there remained no doubt of the approval of Congress.

Denver staged a huge parade and a barbecue picnic in the cottonwood grove on the banks of the Platte. The Masons rode black horses and the Odd Fellows white, the Governor's Guards and the Mitchell Guards marched afoot, and every volunteer fire department crew took part, clad in white or pink trunks and striped jerseys. Boys with firecrackers caused four runaways, and the celebration was a huge success.

On August 1 President Grant issued the admission proclamation and Colorado finally became a state.

Naturally Barney was elated, now that voting equality was guaranteed by the constitution, even though he had worked it out by algebra and had known it to be inevitable. For sixteen years he had worked unceasingly to help his people win this struggle, and now he found himself wishing that Phoebe could know of the victory. He felt that she would be happy and proud to know the part her son had played.

He was led once more into speculating about God's will. It had taken Him a long time, but He had not forgot the black man.

Perhaps God was not the god of the whites, exclusively, but the God of human beings everywhere; white, red, black, yellow. If so, it seemed high time He was doing something for the Indians, who were having a sorry time of it.

The colored people were convinced that the battle for their ballot was won, once and for all, but Barney knew that it would be won only when the First State Legislature adopted adequate election laws. He knew how easily the Negro's gains could be largely nullified by a literacy test or poll tax.

In the last Territorial Legislature the Republicans had controlled the House and the Democrats the Council, which corresponded to a senate. Should the Democrats continue to control one House of the new State Legislature, they could block any controversial election law, so Barney was only too well aware of the importance of electing a Republican majority in both houses. He worked as he had never worked before, and when the returns were all in, the Republicans had won the necessary majority in both houses.

Chaffee was elected to the United States Senate with Henry M. Teller, who later was appointed Secretary of the Interior.

Barney found Wagoner a place as clerk of the legislature. The opposition had taken such a beating that they made no attempt to include an educational test in the election laws.

As approved March 8, 1877, the law gave the vote to all males over twenty-one. This had been Barney's objective ever since coming to Colorado, and for the first time in seventeen years he could really rest content with the knowledge that at last his people were guaranteed the right to vote. During those years he had tasted often of defeat, but as the generals say, it makes no difference how many battles are lost, so long as the final battle is won.

After Congress had outlawed Jim Crow discrimination through passage of the Civil Rights Act, Ed Chase dropped in at the Ford House and invited Barney to visit his gambling house and try his hand at the wheel, but as Barney saw it, the Civil Rights Act had less to do with the invitation than did the fact that he was prosperous, and Chase had an eye on his bankroll.

He thanked him, but told him that ever since his crap-shooting days he had made it a rule never to gamble. Chase conceded that Barney was smarter than he had thought, smart enough to know that he couldn't beat the law of probabilities.

Barney had never mentioned his algebraic method to anyone for fear of being thought eccentric, but now he determined to have a little fun with the gambler, so he asked him if he had ever heard of the law of positivities.

Blinking, Chase admitted that although he had been through college he had never heard of such a law, but he'd damn well like to know about it, for it might prove useful to anyone in his line of business.

Barney had no intention of disclosing the details of his method of calculating the Unknown, for he was saving it for the book he proposed to write when he had perfected his system, but he assured Chase of the existence of such a law, and when the gambler scoffed, offered to prove it.

A city election was to be held shortly, and already Barney had worked it out on paper, so he told Chase what the result would be, but when it resulted just as he had predicted the gambler insisted that he had merely made a lucky guess.

A foot race had been scheduled at the fair grounds between Dougherty and the Hugo Trade Wind and the betting odds favored Dougherty, but Barney was aware of a factor known to no one else. Dougherty's feet were troubling him and he was being treated by a colored corn doctor, so Barney advised Chase to bet on The Trade Wind.

The gambler said that Barney had lost his mind and offered him a personal bet at long odds, but Barney told him that it was against his principles to bet on a sure thing and it would be sinful to win money from those who lacked the benefit of his law of positivities.

When The Trade Wind won, the astonished gambler invited Barney to spend an evening at his place and call the results at roulette, but Barney asserted that roulette was subject to the law of probabilities, about which he knew nothing.

The gambler wanted to test him on something else, but Barney shrewdly refused to crowd his luck, and never thereafter would waste his law of positivities on trivial matters. No one knew if Chase actually had been convinced or if he was merely carrying along a practical joke, but he spread the word that Barney was a wizard with magic powers, and some persons were fool enough to believe it.

They began to come to Barney as if he were a fortune teller, asking him the most absurd questions, like "Does Josie or Effie love me better?" and even offer him money, but he would merely look wise and give them a preposterous answer that they might interpret in any way they chose.

To his astonishment, these gullible ones would delude themselves into thinking that he possessed the gift of clairvoyance and would boast of his power to foretell the future.

They even appealed to him to solve the mystery of the headless dead man. The *News* published an article about a man found in a rooming house with his head cut off and a suicide note claiming that he had cut it off himself and had hid it where no one could find it.

So Barney was asked to use his magic power to discover where the suicide had hid his head. He never doubted that this newspaper story was nothing more than Owen Goldrick's idea of a joke, but unsmilingly he assured his questioners that before coming to Denver the victim had tossed it into the Pacific Ocean.

Finally it reached a point where a woman whose six-year-old daughter was desperately ill with the measles begged him piteously to tell her if the child would live.

Of course he told her that he was no wizard and that Ed Chase had carried a practical joke too far, and thereafter he did his utmost to halt the spread of the ridiculous reports, but the more he denied them the more they were believed.

On the face of the 1876 election returns, it appeared certain that Democrat Sam Tilden had been elected president over Republican Rutherford B. Hayes, but the Hayes supporters charged fraud and demanded a recount. Congress passed an emergency act empowering President Grant to appoint an Electoral Commission to decide the contest.

Meanwhile the Colorado Legislature, which Barney had helped to carry for the Republicans, selected three presidential electors.

As a young lawyer Hayes had represented many runaway slaves who had run afoul of the Fugitive Slave Law, so Barney was among his supporters and prior to the election had organized the Hayes and Wheeler Club among the colored voters.

At the last moment the Electoral Commission ruled that Hayes had won by the margin of one vote in the Electoral College.

Immediately everyone in Colorado began to boast that their state's three Republican electoral votes had sent Hayes to the White House instead of Tilden. Had Colorado failed to win statehood and the Legislature failed to go Republican and choose three Republican electors, Tilden, they maintained, would have won by two electoral votes.

Others made even more extravagant claims. Who was responsible for Colorado's statehood victory? Why, none other than the leader who had swung behind it after twice blocking statehood — Barney L. Ford.

And who was responsible for the election of the three presidential electors who had swung the balance to Hayes? Barney L. Ford, who had fought so strenuously to elect a Republican legislature in order to assure voting equality for his race.

They argued that except for Barney's fight in the Colorado election, Tilden instead of Hayes would have been president of the United States. They recalled that when he blocked statehood in 1866, Andrew Johnson was prevented from being impeached; so scores of persons were boasting that the mulatto runaway slave had become a president-maker, had kept Johnson in office and had sent Hayes to the White House.

Supposedly the decision in favor of Hayes was reached at a meeting of political leaders in the famous old Wormley Hotel at Washington. Here, it was reported, the Democrats were promised that if Hayes were seated he would withdraw the troops from the southern states and restore the functions of the state governments.

This action by Hayes soon after becoming president ended carpetbagger rule, but likewise brought about what Barney had struggled so strenuously to prevent in Colorado, virtual disfranchisement of the colored man in the South by means of poll taxes and literacy tests, a bitter pill for Barney to swallow in view of his pre-election support of Hayes.

The owner of the Wormley Hotel at Washington was William H. A. Wormley, who was to marry Barney's daughter, Sadie.

All the time that Barney had been battling for equal voting rights for his people, he had been waging a parallel struggle to end race segregation in the schools.

It will be recalled that the top-hatted "Professor" Goldrick organized one of Denver's first schools in a log cabin in 1859. Two years later he was one of the group of citizens gathered about a dry goods box in front of a Larimer Street store to organize the first public school system. Goldrick was chosen superintendent of schools for Arapahoe County and organized two school districts, one on either side of Cherry Creek.

He was eminently qualified for the post except for one drawback, his weakness for the flask, and presently found himself separated from the school system and employed in the local room of the *News*.

For some years he remained single, but at middle age married and became a total abstainer. Upon the death of his wife a few years later, the despondent "professor" returned to the habits and companions of his bachelor days.

The earliest Territorial laws set aside in each new mining district one claim adjoining the discovery claim to produce revenue for the public schools, but the revenues were scant and the law was repealed.

At first there was no color line in the schools and no one thought of protesting when young Louis Napoleon Ford attended classes with the white children, but in 1867, when Louis was in the second grade, H. T. Grill and others petitioned the school board of District No. 1 to establish a school for white children exclusively.

The petitioners proposed that the board "invite all the taxpayers opposed to the admission of colored children to the school to apply for the appropriation of the taxes paid by such taxpayers for the support of a school for whites only."

When the board ruled that it lacked power to act on the petition, Superintendent B. D. Hatch, a supporter of segregation, resigned, and all the white pupils walked out on a strike.

Confronted with such a situation, the board reconsidered and decided in favor of segregation, but by rooms rather than by schools. The walkout terminated when the second floor of the school building was set aside for colored children.

The strike evoked so much controversy that the Territorial Legislature adopted a segregation law providing separate schools in districts with fifteen or more colored pupils. Denver and Central City contained the only districts with sufficient pupils to come within the provisions of the segregation law.

Immediately the board of Denver's District No. 1 authorized three schools, including one for colored pupils and another for children of German parentage. The board paid the Zion Baptist Church thirty dollars a month rent for its basement for use as a classroom for the colored children. For a time H. O. Wagoner taught in this school.

In 1872 the school was transferred to the basement of the African M. E. Church, where Louis, Sadie, and Frankie Ford attended classes.

Construction of a pretentious brick school building was begun on Arapahoe Street, but before it was completed the district ran short of funds. Barney was among the signers of a petition asking that a bond issue be submitted to the voters, providing funds to finish the building.

He was disturbed at the prospect that a color line might bar Louis, Sadie, and Frankie from this school, so he circulated a petition pointing out that the constitution guaranteed equal rights, and asking that "scholars be classified according to merit and attainment alone."

When the Arapahoe Street school opened its doors, no color line existed, no segregation by rooms.

Under provisions of the state segregation law, separate schools had been established at Central City, but as the mining boom subsided the colored school was closed because the number of pupils fell below the satutory limit of fifteen, but when the Negro children presented themselves at the white school they were denied admission by the white teachers.

Their parents retained 39-year-old Henry M. Teller, the future United States Senator and Secretary of the Interior, and when he threatened to bring a damage suit, members of the board speedily changed their minds.

The two local newspapers, the *Register* and the Colorado *Herald*, both favoring segregation, concluded that the only course was to establish another school to be paid for by those objecting to sending their youngsters to the same school with colored children.

Down in the valley at Idaho Springs no color line had been drawn, since the district was too small to come within the statutory limitation. In the midst of a school entertainment in 1871, the schoolmistress announced that the white pupils had refused to take part because a little mulatto boy was on the program, and she lost her temper and charged the parents with instigating the "strike."

For a few minutes the parents argued hotly, but sympathy was with the colored lad, who began to sob. Finally he was permitted to speak his piece, and he wiped away his tears and gave the recitation the best that was in him. Most of the audence applauded and said he had done wonderfully well, and it was a pity that he wasn't white, or he would be certain to make his mark in the world.

To Barney it was a heartbreaking example of cruel prejudice. He had taken his share of humiliation and hard knocks because of his color, but he could fight back.

But here was this little mulatto, the brightest lad in school, with perhaps the potentials of a Michelangelo or a Shakespeare or an Abraham Lincoln, but he might as well have been born with a ball and chain riveted to him.

A few more like experiences and the boy's spirit would be crushed and he might be doomed to spend his life shining shoes for a living when he might have been another Daniel Webster. Perhaps, thought Barney, the incident had marked the crushing of a human spirit. Perhaps a potential Daniel Webster had died there.

In Denver, the *News* became righteously indignant about the affair, and in view of Byers' recent "nigger" editorials, his change of heart was astonishing.

> We would remind some of the older heads who are so blinded by prejudice, that the war is over, slavery is abolished, and hundreds of mulattoes and even full-blooded Africans, can teach them lessons of godliness, general intelligence and respectability, and that if they possessed the first principle of human charity or one grain of Christian virtue, it would crimson their frowning visages with blushes at their own ignorance and brand them with eternal shame and disgrace because of their ungodly prejudice.

Even before Colorado became a state, plans had been made to establish a state university. Barney had assumed that the issue of race equality had been settled by the three Reconstruction amendments and by the equal rights guarantee in the state constitution.

As introduced in the last Territorial legislature, the state university bill contained an anti-discrimination clause, but on motion to strike the clause, two Democrats joined with the Council Republicans in voting *no;* but the motion carried by a single vote, and Barney was astounded when it likewise passed the Republican House.

Charging that the color line had been drawn at the state university, the *News* branded it a "highty-tighty" thing to do, a Democratic trick, an act of unseemly prejudice against the "despised race." Byers alleged that they wanted to keep the colored people in bondage of ignorance because they knew Negroes to be more intelligent than Democrats, but he neglected to note that the Republican House had voted the same as the Democratic Council.

When the University of Colorado opened its doors at Boulder in 1877, young Louis Ford was ready to enter college. No one was certain whether the state constitution had nullified the act of the Territorial Legislature in drawing the color line at the institution, so to be on the safe side Barney sent his son to Howard University at Washington, D. C., where brilliant young Henry Wagoner had won his law degree.

If the University of Colorado ever actually drew the color line, the records fail to show it. In later years the university never practiced race discrimination, and turned out many distinguished Negro graduates.

Barney's Inter-Ocean Hotel had proven itself such a civic asset that Cheyenne became envious, and its Chamber of Commerce wanted a hotel as good or better. Who could build it for them? Who but Barney Ford? So the chamber proposed to donate the site if he would build the hotel.

XVII

The business depression following the collapse of Cheyenne's early railroad boom had become less noticeable as vast herds of cattle were trailed into the Territory from Texas. Originally in Dakota Territory, Cheyenne now was in Wyoming Territory, created in 1868.

The new prosperity based on the growing livestock industry tempted Barney. He had profited on the Inter-Ocean Hotel deal in Denver, and reasoned that he could do as well at Cheyenne.

He mortgaged some of his Denver property to raise capital for the Cheyenne venture, but continued to operate Ford's Hotel at Denver.

The new hotel, also called the Inter-Ocean, was one of Cheyenne's most pretentious structures, even boasting a tank on the roof to supply running water for all the rooms. It cost Barney $65,000.

Upon its opening in the summer of 1875, even the newspapers back in "the states" took notice. The Chicago *Inter-ocean* published an article stating that "Mister Ford certainly knew how to keep hotel and would give the public the squarest meal between two oceans." Julia pasted the clipping in her scrap book.

The Inter-Ocean was near the railroad station, where all the Union Pacific and Denver Pacific trains stopped thirty minutes for meals. Barney kept the restaurant open all night for the railroad trade; and, to attract the night passengers, he installed what the newspapers claimed to be the first illuminated sign in Wyoming Territory.

All the principal banquets and balls were held at the Inter-

Ocean, and each Thursday evening the Pleasant Hours Social Dancing Club staged a hop in the ballroom.

Once more Barney found himself shuttling back and forth between Cheyenne and Denver, looking after his business interests, but now he was riding on the Denver Pacific instead of bouncing about in a stagecoach.

Periodically President Grant toured the West to keep an ear to the ground and an eye on the state chairmen. In April of 1873 he made his second visit to Denver, accompanied by his wife and his daughter, Nellie.

A member of the reception committee with Governor Elbert and former Governor Evans was Barney's friend, Wagoner, who was thrilled to shake the hand of the president who, as general, had written him the letter of commendation during the war. Everyone noted the resemblance of Grant and Publisher Byers.

In October of 1875 the President made another swing through the West, and Cheyenne made eager preparations to entertain the distinguished guest. Naturally the President was to be entertained at the leading hotel, the Inter-Ocean.

The presidential train was due to arrive shortly before noon on October 4, The reception committee planned an elaborate dinner at the Inter-Ocean, to be followed by a reception in the hotel parlors.

Barney was prepared to provide a dinner that would make Wyoming history, with antelope steaks and mountain trout and claret and champagne. But somehow someone on the presidential special became confused and neglected to notify the reception committee of a change in schedule, so instead of arriving at noon the President's train rolled in at half past seven in the morning.

The emergency left Barney undismayed. Within twenty minutes after the presidential carriage appeared at the door, he served a sumptuous breakfast and by the time the reception was held in the hotel parlors members of the committee agreed that he had saved the day.

Grant said that he remembered Barney from the banquet in

Denver in 1868 and assured him that no hotel keeper in Washington or even New York could equal him, so naturally Barney was pleased.

About this time he received word through his Denver lawyer that Claiborne had died, not only without a dollar, but with extensive debts. Times were none too good, the country having failed to recover from the effects of the panic of 1873. Barney had borrowed heavily for his Cheyenne venture, was short of ready cash, and was under considerable expense, with Louis at the university, but he could not bring himself to permit his own half-brother to be buried in a pauper's grave.

He signed another note at the bank and directed his lawyer to send the funds for funeral expenses and promised to care for Claiborne's debts in the course of time. No one in Charleston was aware that the mulatto runaway slave provided the money to bury his former white master and to pay his debts.

The death of his white half-brother led Barney to further serious thinking about the Hereafter. He remembered the Claiborne of prewar days as a decent sort of a person and had no reason to believe that he had changed. The half-brother had done right as he saw it, and, even though Claiborne had owned slaves, Barney hoped that a just God would not condemn him. Perhaps God would hold that his years of poverty made up for his earlier mistakes.

What, he asked himself, if one does what he believes to be right, according to the way he has been taught, and then it develops that what he held to be right was actually wrong? Will God hold it against him, punish him for something he didn't know?

Was Heaven reserved for everyone opposed to slavery, and hell for the Southern Democrats and former slave owners who perhaps knew no better? If God barred the ignorant from Heaven, how many would be left?

What if, upon finding himself in the Hereafter, Claiborne discovered, as some of Barney's algebraic research had led him to suspect, that God was not white?

Barney had never been able to learn if Claiborne ever knew or guessed that the mulatto slave boy was his half-brother. Did he know it now?

174

Some believe that the souls of the departed can look down on earth and know what is passing in anyone's mind. Would Claiborne be surprised to discover that his black half-brother had paid for his funeral? Would he be grateful, or would it anger him?

Had he carried his pride with him into the Hereafter perhaps he would not approve of Barney's action. In some ways, Barney thought, Claiborne was due for some startling and unpleasant surprises.

What if he discovered that no color line exists in the Hereafter? What if the souls of Old Missy and Claiborne were the same color as the souls of Phoebe and the other slaves? What would Claiborne think of that? What if, from the beginning of time, there had been a Civil Rights Act in Heaven?

These questions Barney was unable to answer offhand. He sat down with his pencil and attempted to work it out by algebra, but there were too many unknown factors.

He was just beginning to make progress with his law of positivities in learning about more important matters than whether he was to make money or win an election, but before he could proceed much further it would be necessary to work on many missing factors.

For the last few years he had been so occupied with business affairs that he had devoted little time to his algebra. Now he set himself to make up for lost time, but his interest was centered on searching into the Hereafter.

Even though he was spending most of his time in Cheyenne, he had not given up his Denver home and still maintained his voting residence there, and in 1874 he took an active part in the city election campaign.

The coming of the railroads in 1870 had sent Denver real estate values soaring, but the panic of '73 punctured the boom. The value of Barney's real estate holdings had shrunk by more than half, and most of his improved property had been mortgaged to finance the Cheyenne hotel.

To make matters worse, the farmers were suffering from a series of droughts and grasshopper plagues. In Cheyenne business was at a standstill and the Inter-Ocean was not making expenses.

Barney was certain that if he could hold out for another year or so, business was sure to pick up. To keep the Cheyenne hotel in operation he sold his Denver hotel at a loss, but it proved to be throwing good money after bad. The mortgage on his Curtis Street home was foreclosed, and Julia moved to Cheyenne with Sadie and Frankie to reduce expenses.

A few years earlier Barney had been worth all of a quarter of a million. Now he found himself on the verge of bankruptcy. Moreover, he was in his late fifties.

Julia willingly resumed waiting on table in the hotel dining room, but forbade Sadie and Frankie to follow her example, for she wished them to obtain a good education, like Louis, and grow up to be ladies.

Louis was training himself to enter the hotel business, like his father, and Barney had always looked forward to the time when he could retire and turn his affairs over to his son, but now it appeared that Louis might be compelled to leave the university before winning his degree.

Barney kept holding to the Cheyenne Inter-Ocean, hoping that business would improve. He spent his spare time perfecting his algebra system, preparing for the time when he could explain it in his book.

Down across the Colorado boundary the Utes were threatening to jump the reservation. Some years earlier the government had given them most of western Colorado for their reservation, promising them $25,000 a year in annuity goods. But upon the discovery of gold in the San Juan district the Indians were persuaded to relinquish that part of their reservation.

Colorado residents became convinced that the entire reservation contained mineral deposits as rich as those of the San Juan country and persuaded themselves that exploitation of these fancied resources would bring millions into the state treasury and would reduce taxes accordingly. The newspapers began to damn the Utes as bloodthirsty savages and to demand that they be banished from the reservation. Everyone that lost a horse attributed it to the thieving red devils, and whenever lightning started a forest fire the Indians received the blame.

Oddly enough, although the Utes ranged northward through Wyoming, the residents of that state regarded them as mild and harmless, for Wyoming had nothing to gain by expelling them from the reservation. Coloradans were greedy for supposed mineral riches and hoped to reduce their taxes by exploiting the reservation, so in Colorado the Ute was regarded as a bloodthirsty barbarian.

Ouray was chief of the tribe, and under him was the leader of the White River Utes, Captain Jack, who could speak fair English. The Utes sent Captain Jack to Denver to negotiate with the governor. The Indians merely wished to be let alone and to receive the annuity goods that had been promised them.

The railroad town closest to the White River Agency was Laramie, Wyoming, where the Utes were supposed to receive annuity goods that the government promised but seldom delivered because unscrupulous government employees and dishonest contractors helped themselves first.

Captain Jack took the train for Denver by way of Cheyenne, where it was necessary to lay over between trains. Learning that he was waiting at the station, Barney brought him to the hotel and fed him and began to question him about the red man's concept of God.

Captain Jack talked freely, perhaps because he believed Barney to be part Indian. He hated all whites, and at each mention of them would touch his tongue with two fingers, the sign language indication for "man who speaks with a forked tongue," or liar.

Presently Barney led him to talk about the Happy Hunting Grounds. Were whites admitted, or only Indians? Was it true that a Manitou or Great Spirit was supreme, like the white man's God?

Sure there was a Great Spirit, but not like the white man's God, by damn. The Great Spirit wasn't cruel, and if he promised plenty buffalo, that's the way it would be.

Was his skin the same color as the Indians'?

How could anyone ask such a foolish question? Sure.

Then he was not the same Great Spirit that the white man worshiped?

Hell, no. Only the God of the white man was white.

Then there was a black God for black men?

Captain Jack supposed so, although he had given it no thought. Did everyone go to the Happy Hunting Grounds when he died?

Well, practically. Of course if one were killed in battle and the enemy took his scalp, it stood to reason that he couldn't get there unless someone returned the scalp to his squaw.

Then what happened to these excluded souls? Did they go to hell?

No, they just hung around outside, making the best of things. Only the white man had a hell, a place of everlasting torture, but even the fear of burning forever failed to prevent the whites from being cruel and wicked. He supposed that the red man had no hell because none deserved to go there.

Barney thanked Captain Jack and gave him a one-pound sack of smoking tobacco. The Ute leader proceeded to Denver but the governor, instead of receiving him as one chief receives another, kept him waiting in the outer office for two days.

Captain Jack had the impudence to tell him that if the whites would only keep their promises and send the overdue annuity goods, he could guarantee peace, but when the bellies of the squaws and papooses were flat from starvation, the braves were bound to jump the reservation and kill some white man's cattle, and that meant war.

Also he had the effrontery to claim that a reservation is not merely a place to keep the Indians confined, but is a place from which the greedy white men should be excluded.

He even went so far as to claim that a treaty is a pledge of honor between nations, not something to bind one and not the other. To cap it all, he warned that if white soldiers crossed the reservation boundary it would constitute an act of war.

Despite his warning, troops were sent in from Fort Steele, and when they crossed the reservation boundary the Utes ambushed them, killed many, massacred Indian Agent Nathan Meeker and every white man at the agency, and kidnaped three white women. So the government was provided with an excuse to move the tribe to tiny reservations in Utah and southwestern Colorado and to open western Colorado to the whites. They failed to find the expected gold or to gain a reduction in taxes.

Barney was convinced that Captain Jack was more intelligent than the governor or the Washington officeholders, and felt that had his advice been followed the Meeker massacre would have been avoided.

Captain Jack disliked being cooped up on the tiny Utah reservation, so he departed for a visit with friends on the Wind River reservation in Wyoming. The whites assumed that he was planning to incite the Arapahoes and Shoshones and sent a detachment of troops after him.

They found him in a tepee with his friends and ordered him to come out and surrender, but he was conscious of no offense for which he should surrender, so they opened fire with a Gatling gun and blew the tepee to bits with everyone in it and so Captain Jack learned at first hand about the Happy Hunting Grounds.

Business failed to improve as Barney had hoped. The holders of the mortgage on the Inter-Ocean were becoming impatient, and finally he made a settlement leaving them in possession of the hotel.

As bride and bridegroom he and Julia had dreamed of seeking their fortune in the California gold fields, only to be diverted into the hotel business in Nicaragua by his illness. Now he was taken with another relapse of the gold fever.

California's early-day gold fields had been pretty well worked out, but occasionally he heard rumors of new strikes, and he could always fall back on the restaurant business. What matter his fifty-seven years?

With Julia and his daughters he went to San Francisco, where he rented a tiny lunch counter at 118 Post Street. So Barney, recently a bank trustee and owner of two large hotels, found himself back in the kitchen once more, frying hamburgers. Julia, who had lived in one of Denver's most sumptuous homes, had become a waitress again.

Barney was untroubled, for he had worked out an equation and knew he was to become rich once more. Soon he read of the strike at Bodie. Leaving Sadie and Frankie with friends at San Francisco, he and Julia struck out for the new gold field.

It proved to be Mountain City and Breckenridge all over again.

Too late to get in on the ground floor, he opened the Chop Stand lunch counter and did fairly well.

The few weeks he spent at Bodie were not wasted, for it was there that he made friends with Lee Wong, the laundryman, and learned something of a Buddhist's conception of the Hereafter.

No, Gautama Buddha was not a god; merely a prophet and teacher. Each person has two souls, one good and one bad, and the bad one is in for a hard time of it in the Hereafter. These two souls were always at odds, and if Barney's bad soul got the best of his good one, he might be reborn as a pig or a slave.

Well, then, the reason someone is born a slave is because in his next preceding life his bad soul has overcome his good soul. Is that right?

Sure, that's it, Barney, but it's nothing to worry about. In one of his five hundred and fifty incarnations Buddha himself was a slave, but likewise he had been an ape, an elephant, a crow, a frog, and a king.

If he lived an upright life, then, a slave stood a chance of becoming a king in his next incarnation?

Well, just ordinary upright people were due to be born again as a man. The unusually virtuous might be reborn as Chinese.

Then there was no color line in the Buddhist Hereafter?

No, not in the way Barney meant, for the Hereafter was a succession of incarnations, and he might be white in one, black in another and, if unusually pious, a yellow man. Of course, he might have been all these colors in the Heretofore.

This mention of the Heretofore interested Barney, since it was related to his algebraic system. None of his research had led him to doubt the existence of God; on the contrary, his algebra could prove God's existence. One cannot identify Infinity by the evidence of the senses, but algebra can prove its existence. Likewise one cannot see God, but can prove that He exists.

Well, then, what is the Infinite? Something without limit, without beginning or end. What is the Hereafter? Life everlasting, without end.

But Now is the beginning of the Hereafter. How can anything

have a beginning but no end? If it has either beginning or end, it has a limit and hence cannot be infinite.

The same is true of the Heretofore. It has an end but not a beginning, so it cannot be infinite.

But the Heretofore and the Hereafter together constitute the Infinite, something with neither beginning nor end.

If so, what? It was an interesting field for algebraic exploration, nothing more. His interest was centered on the Hereafter.

Even so, he felt that he was coming closer and closer to the solution of the Big Problem that was to make the book he planned to write one of the most important books ever written.

Hardly had he set himself up in business at Bodie when he read in the newspapers of a new gold and silver discovery at the familiar old mining camp, Breckenridge, Colorado. Immediately he worked out an equation.

It was the same that he had worked twice previously, and both times it had indicated that he was to find riches at Breckenridge. Twice something had gone wrong, so now he worked and reworked the equation, and each time the result was the same; he was to get rich at Breckenridge. He boarded the next eastbound train.

XVIII

He found Breckenridge experiencing its third mining boom. Will Iliff, member of the original discovery party in 1859, had been puttering about ever since, but without luck until he returned in 1878 and discovered the Blue Danube quartz lode on Shock Hill, across the gulch from Nigger Hill.

Prior to Barney's arrival on April 17, 1880, gold had been discovered in half a dozen additional fissure and vein formaitons. Already 6,190 location certificates had been filed and more than one hundred mining companies had been organized.

A few years earlier Breckenridge had become almost a ghost town, but now it boasted a population of two thousand. More than one hundred buildings were under construction.

H. A. W. Tabor, who had filed in the Arazonia district on one of the first silver claims twenty years earlier, was back again, and owned a share of the Columbia mine on Nigger Hill and an interest in other Breckenridge properties. He had struck it rich at Leadville, was known as the bonanza king and was on his way to the United States Senate.

The treasurer of the Atlantic & Pacific Mining & Tunnel Company was operating a modest clothing store at Leadville. His Breckenridge property proved to be worthless, but he kept expanding his clothing business until it became the greatest chain of department stores in the United States. Its name is the May Department Stores and he was David May, but since he had yet to gain riches, he was called merely Dave.

The Helen mine, not far from the spot from which Barney and his friends had been ejected by Dode in 1860, was one of the leading producers in French Gulch. On Nigger Hill were several rich properties, including the Autocrat, Breckenridge Belle, Powhatan, Laurium, and Maggie.

F. W. Pitkin, former governor, was president of the two-million-dollar Ballarat. While still governor, he had donned overalls and wielded a muck-stick in this mine.

Riethmann, Barney's former tenant and business associate, was wealthy now, a Denver banker and part owner of both the Riethmann-Ebert placer and the Helen and Mineral Hill group of mines.

Tom Patterson, the Democrat who defeated Bromwell for delegate to Congress in 1874, barring the colored man "Judge" Budd from possible appointment as minister to Haiti, was part owner of the Silver Glance and of the Washington and Hancock group.

He had taken over the Rocky Mountain *News* from go-betweens who had bought it from Byers and had changed its politics, and as the state's leading Democrat was making life hard for the Republicans. Everyone knew that he was ambitious to go to the United States Senate but felt that he stood little chance because he was a Democrat, but in the long run he whipped the Republicans soundly and achieved his ambition.

Barney rented a one-story frame building and called it Ford's Chop House. Presently Julia and Sadie joined him and they lived in the rear of the restaurant. Sadie, who possessed a sweet voice like her mother's, sang soprano in the church choir. Louis was still attending the university and Frankie had remained in San Francisco with kinfolk.

Financially Barney was near bedrock when he went to Breckenridge for his third attempt to get rich there. In his days of prosperity he had paid $3,500 for seven unimproved lots in Denver's Chattenham Heights, but now he gladly sold them for a thousand dollars, which represented his entire capital when he established himself in business again.

He was scarcely settled before the *News* published an article telling how the group of colored prospectors had discovered gold in French Gulch twenty years earlier, had been forced out, and had buried their gold on Nigger Hill, now honeycombed with rich mines.

Barney's name was not mentioned, but there were still some Breckenridge residents, like Will Iliff, who remembered him from the early days. Whether it was started by Iliff no one knows, but presently the rumor spread about that Barney had returned to Breckenridge to dig up that cache of gold buried on Nigger Hill back in 1860.

At first the rumor amounted to little, but Ford's Chop House was prospering, although Barney was far from becoming rich as the law of positivities had given him the right to expect. Within a year he bought the restaurant building.

By September of 1881 he bought the Oyster Ocean restaurant in Denver and began to divide his time between the two towns. The following year he built one of the finest small homes in Breckenridge, and the Summit County *Journal* wrote that it recalled the houses in the Sunny South "where lavish nature has been supplemented by generations of culture." The article noted that the luxury of Barney's home "deprives us of the power to realize that we are in the land of log cabins and tented homes." Julia and Sadie always returned to Denver in the winter.

Some time before Barney's new home was completed, the Breckenridge bank closed its doors and the cashier vanished. At about the same time several Leadville banks collapsed. Times were hard and cash was scarce.

Quite naturally everyone began to wonder about Barney's apparent prosperity. There seemed but one explanation; he was drawing upon that cache of hidden gold on Nigger Hill.

Rumor had it that $100,000 in gold dust was hidden on the mountainside and that whenever Barney needed cash he needed only to withdraw it from the cache. The rumors did no injury to his credit, so when the curious would attempt to worm from him a hint as to where the gold was buried, he would merely wink and say nothing.

The stage was reached where he could not go out at night without someone following him, certain that he was sneaking away to draw on his reserve supply of gold dust. Once or twice, to amuse himself, he would strike out toward Nigger Hill and lose himself in the timber, merely to lead these gullible treasure-seekers on a wild goose chase.

It was carrying things too far when someone seeking the supposed treasure burglarized his restaurant, so he began to deny the gold dust rumor, insisting that it was nothing but a joke.

As was the case in Denver when he denied being a wizard, the more he denied, the wilder grew the rumors. So many miners quit their jobs to search for his buried treasure that the sides of Nigger Hill were pock-marked with the holes they dug.

In 1882 Barney bought the Horseshoe mine on Bald Mountain, and the purchase served only to incite further rumors. Actually it was a minor transaction, a gamble that never paid out, for all that he ever took from the Horseshoe was debt. He was far from becoming rich again as the law of positivities had promised.

In January of 1882 he took Julia to the banquet in Denver of the Colorado Association of Pioneers, and it was a noteworthy event in their lives.

When the pioneers organized in 1872 the constitution limited membership to "white male citizens who became residents prior to December 31, 1860." Publisher Byers was the first secretary.

Despite being on opposing sides in the statehood fights, Byers and Barney were close friends. By the time Colorado became a state, the publisher had changed his mind about many matters and thought it shameful that the color of his skin barred Barney from the Pioneers, so in 1876 he introduced a resolution to eliminate the word "white" so Barney could join the organization.

The members argued over parliamentary procedure and held that the proposal should have been offered as a constitutional amendment, which required a two-thirds vote for passage. The action hurt Barney deeply, even though he was accustomed to such rebuffs.

In 1881 Wolfe Londoner, the grocer, finally succeeded in changing the association constitution so Barney could be admitted. The same year women were admitted as honorary members. Julia was ineligible, since she had not reached Colorado until 1861, a few months too late to qualify, but as Barney's wife she could attend the annual banquet. They were the first members of their race ever to attend this affair.

In October of 1883 a decision of the United States Supreme Court seriously crippled the Fourteenth Amendment, holding that it did not guarantee civil rights to the Negro. The court ruled that "individual invasion of individual rights is not the subject matter of the amendment," which merely prohibits "state action of a particular character." In other words, the Federal government could take no action on civil rights unless a state first overstepped the line.

The decision was another setback for Barney. There was little he could do but organize a movement to induce the State Legislature to adopt a civil rights act.

Two years later, in 1885, the act was approved, with a fine or jail term for denying the colored man equal rights in "hotels, restaurants, churches, barber shops, public conveyances, theaters or other places of public resort or amusement."

Barney sold his Oyster Ocean restaurant in Denver, and his son, Louis, found a hotel job at Salida. The Denver & South Park railroad had been completed from Denver to Breckenridge in 1882, its narrow-gauge tracks winding down across the slopes of Nigger Hill.

Barney moved to larger quarters and called his new Main Street restaurant the Saddle Rock. Two or three times a year he and Julia would hold parties for the Breckenridge children at their home and stuff them with popcorn and apples. They loved to hear him tell stories, some of which were of his own invention.

Twice a year, in spring and fall, a family living far back in the hills would drive to Breckenridge to lay in supplies. They always brought their children and the grandfather, Tobe, who had been totally blind for twenty years, the consequence of thawing dynamite in a frying pan. They always had one meal at the Saddle Rock, and then Tobe and the youngsters would remain with Barney while the couple spent the afternoon buying corn meal and salt and calico and tobacco.

Barney was telling the children the story of the Babes in The Wood, and they were frightened at the thought that they might be eaten by a bear, and said that they didn't want to die.

Blind grandpa Tobe, seated in a rocker sucking an empty corncob pipe, suddenly demanded, why was anyone afraid to die? He wasn't. In fact, he was all eagerness to learn what conditions prevailed on yon side of the Great Divide, since he had been living in hell for twenty years.

Barney suggested that it was only the wicked that were really afraid to die, and not the God-fearing ones.

Tobe asked, why should anybody fear Him if God dealt out justice without fear or favor? Personally he felt that God gave everybody a square deal, so he wasn't afraid of Him, but instead had a mighty friendly feeling toward Him. He admitted that if he had had his sight he might have got into some sort of devilment that would have troubled his conscience and made him a God-fearing man afraid to die.

Barney could not agree with his theory. He had done some things of which he was ashamed — not many that might be called downright wicked — but still he did not care to go to Heaven just yet.

For one thing, he wanted to write that book so everyone could benefit from what he had learned of the law of positivities — not to mention getting rich again. Now he inquired about Tobe's idea of Heaven.

Well, replied the blind man, it was a place with lots of light where everybody could see, and if perhaps you had lost a leg in a railroad accident, well, you'd have that leg when you got Over There. Everyone would be physically perfect. God would see to that.

Now Barney was getting closer to what he really wanted to know. What did Tobe think God looks like?

The reply startled him. Why did Barney say He? How did he know that God wasn't a woman?

Barney pointed out that the Bible said God created man in His own image. The blind man said that meant mankind, not just male, and women were a part of mankind, weren't they? And how did he get around that?

Barney said he wasn't trying to get around it, but was curious about one thing; did God belong to the white race or the black, to the red or to the yellow?

Since Barney's speech was so precise and because the old man was blind, it was impossible for Tobe to know that he was being questioned by a colored man. He wanted to know what difference it made, so Barney told him that it might make a great deal of difference to a colored man.

Tobe said he'd just as soon take his chances with a colored God. Having seen no colors for half a lifetime, he doubted that anyone's color mattered especially.

To put it another way, he supposed that every human being conceived of a God like that person wished himself to be. In a way of speaking, everyone made his own God.

If you believed God to be a terrible, vengeful Being waiting to cast you down into hell because you had forgot to say your prayers once when you were eight years old, that was the kind of God you would probably encounter in the Hereafter.

Or if you believed Him to be just and fair to everyone regardless of politics or color, that's the way it would be.

He didn't intend to be sacrilegious, but he was thinking of a prospector he once knew who argued that if man was created in the image of God, that meant that God had a mouth, which in turn implied that He liked good things to eat like everyone else, and maybe even enjoyed a good cigar now and then. Did Barney think that Tobe was sacrilegious or disrespectful?

Instead of believing in a segregated Hereafter like Captain Jack, old Tobe seemed to believe in millions of Heavens, each made to order for the individual. Barney failed to agree with his theories, but that evening he set down some notes for his book and worked out some new equations, but made little progress. There still remained too many unknown factors to get a satisfactory answer to his inquiry into the Hereafter.

He returned to something simpler: the old problem of getting rich at Breckenridge. It brought the same result as before, a positive, affirmative answer.

But he was becoming more and more impatient, for he was sixty-two years old and still unable to begin work on his book. Julia was putting on weight and was short of breath at the 10,-000-foot elevation and longed to live in Denver the year 'round.

Once in Denver and once in Cheyenne Barney's property had been wiped out by fire. In 1887 fire swept the business district of Breckenridge. He saved most of the restaurant equipment and, when Main Street was rebuilt, moved into larger quarters.

He had almost forgot his experience in Nicaragua, but in 1887 he read an article in the *News* about the incorporation in Denver of a twelve-million-dollar concern called the Nicaragua Canal Construction Company, organized to complete the canal originally contemplated by Commodore Vanderbilt. The Wall Street capitalists behind the company spent four millions on new surveys, but the French company under De Lesseps that was building the Panama Canal failed, selling its property and concessions to the United States government, so plans for the Nicaragua Canal were abandoned.

Not far from the spot where Barney had panned his first gold in French Gulch was the Oro group of mines, including the Oro, Siam, Chief, and Diamond Dick lode mining claims. John J. Mairs, who owned a fifteen-thirty-seconds interest in the group offered to sell out to Barney for $4,000.

After working another simple equation, he became convinced that he should close the deal. He could raise only $1,350 in cash and wished that the buried treasure rumor had been true. He argued Mairs down to $3,750, paid him the $1,350 cash and gave him a mortgage for the remaining $2,400.

Owners of the majority interest were Captain George L. Ryan, a Union veteran, and John B. Harlow. Barney was convinced that this was the deal that was to make him rich once more.

Mining activity had tapered off during the mid-eighties, but no one in Breckenridge, including Barney, would admit it. He talked optimistically to every stranger visiting the Saddle Rock. A visitor from New York state who wore corduroy pants, high lace boots, and pince-nez showed some interest and inquired about local mining properties. His name was James J. Welch.

Barney advised him that the Oro was a promising property and might be picked up cheap for perhaps a couple hundred thousand. Welch appeared uninterested when he departed from Breckenridge, but within a few weeks a mining engineer appeared and inspected the Oro, to be followed by a lawyer who said he represented a client who was prepared to pay $50,000 for the property.

Ryan, Harlow, and Barney set $200,000 as the minimum price they would accept, kept negotiating with the lawyer, and finally settled on $100,000. On March 5, 1889, the lawyer bought an option for $10,000 and the same day Barney paid off his $2,400 loan from his share of the payment and spent the next ninety days on pins and needles hoping that the deal would go through.

Welch represented a group of wealthy investors from Syracuse, New York, and before the option expired they paid the remainder of the $100,000.

Barney had invested only $1,350 of his own money in the Oro, and his net return in two years was $44,460. As the equation had indicated, he was rich once more.

Twenty-nine years had elapsed since it had first come out that he was to find riches at Breckenridge. Never again could he doubt the effectiveness of his law of positivities.

The new owners took possession of the Oro on June 10 and immediately encountered trouble. A. J. Heaton and Charles Shipley claimed to own one of the claims and were prepared to protect their rights with gunplay. Barney and his partners had agreed to deliver the Oro with a clear title, so they brought a $4,500 lawsuit against Heaton and Shipley and finally won a clear title.

After the mining sale, one of Barney's first acts was to have a nugget of pure gold from the Oro made into a watch charm, and he was accustomed to toy with it as Big Thompson had once toyed with his own charm. He established Louis Napoleon in the hotel business at Jefferson City, Missouri, but Louis never equalled his father in the hotel field.

Frankie had married in San Francisco and was expecting. Sadie had been keeping company in Denver with Ed Sanderlin's son, Willie, but the affair came to an abrupt end when she began to accept the attentions of a white man.

Barney had nothing against this young fellow, but he liked Sanderlin and Sanderlin's son. Most colored parents would have been delighted to have a daughter marry a white man, but not Barney and Julia. They were proud of their Negro blood.

Nevertheless, they were not prejudiced against the whites. All his life Barney had fought against race prejudice, and he had learned it can work both ways. So far as he and Julia were concerned, it was none of their business, only Sadie's.

On one of his winter trips to Denver, Julia let him know that Sadie's young white friend wished to talk with him. Barney was certain that he could guess the purpose of the interview but did not propose to stand in the way of his daughter's happiness.

The young fellow was awaiting him in the front parlor and chatted nervously about the weather and mining before finally coming to the point. All his white friends would look down on him if he married a mulatto girl, but nevertheless he was quite willing to marry Sadie in return for $40,000.

All his life Barney had trained himself to swallow insults and remain calm, but this once he lost control of himself. Seizing the young man by the collar, he flung him from the front door and warned him that if ever he spoke another word to Sadie, Barney would put a bullet through him.

Sadie was broken-hearted when she learned that the young man wanted $40,000 to marry her. To get her mind off the break-up of her two love affairs, Barney sent her to Chicago, where Julia's family found a job for her. Before long she was being courted by William H. A. Wormley, the wealthy Washington hotel owner.

Since the altitude at Breckenridge was too much for Julia, Barney sold the Saddle Rock and moved back to Denver.

Strangely enough, as it developed some years later, he never owned legal title to this restaurant, to his Breckenridge home, or to his interest in the Oro because Breckenridge was not in United States territory!

Some lawyers examining the titles of mining properties discovered that some two thousand square miles in Summit and Grand counties was a No Man's land lying between the territories acquired by the Louisiana Purchase and the Texas annexation.

The Federal government had never acquired title to this land through deed or gift, purchase or treaty. Since it had been part of the original Ute reservation, the Indians might have claimed it had they retained a competent lawyer.

The United States Attorney General handed down an opinion that the territory could be annexed, so Governor Edwin C. Johnson and representatives of the army and navy formally took possession and raised the flag of the United States over the courthouse.

All this took place long after Barney's return to Denver, prepared to retire again and to devote his time to writing his book.

XIX

Barney and Julia bought a home at 1569 High Street, in the heart of Denver's choicest Capitol Hill residence district. It was far from Five Points, where the colored population now centered after shifting from the Deep South segregated district. Their white neighbors raised no objection to the presence of the Negro family.

Everyone liked and respected Barney and the soft-spoken Julia. His hair and goatee were white now, for he was sixty-eight years old. Thicker through the waist, he still carried himself rigidly erect.

He dressed in good taste and drove a fine carriage. Neither Barney nor Julia ever sought to intrude where they were not wanted, so they got along pleasantly enough with their white neighbors.

Before he could settle down to writing his book, Barney still had some business affairs to settle. He sold his Breckenridge home and made a small profit on some lots on the bank of the Blue, but might have made far more by holding the property a few years longer until the gold dredges came into the valley.

Back in the early sixties it was assumed that the Long Toms had stripped the sandbars of all their placer gold, but placer mining was far from the point of exhaustion.

Soon after the huge gold boat dredges were developed, they commenced to gnaw deep into the beds of the streams, tearing at the banks, swallowing the gold and spitting out the sand and rock.

Finally the dredges closed in on Breckenridge from both upstream and downstream, greedy for the gold that lay under the river-bank property, so the owners sold out to the dredging companies and the gold boats gnawed away a sizeable section of the town, buildings and all, including the lots that Barney once owned.

193

The new owners of the Oro desired some prominent, respected Coloradan identified with the company, so they employed Barney as their local representative, and he was kept so busy shuttling back and forth between the mine and Denver that he was left with little time to devote to his book.

He was a grandfather now, and of course took Julia to San Francisco to see the new grandchild, Edith, whose eyes were blue and whose hair was blonde.

About the time that the Fords returned to Denver, the newspapers were filled with reports of the new gold strike at Cripple Creek, and Barney was eager to try his luck in the new field. Julia was flatly opposed to any such venture. At their age they could not afford to lose, and if they won, what more would money bring them?

So Barney worked another equation, but the answer discouraged him. Nevertheless he might have tried his luck at Cripple Creek, except for fear that if the answer to the equation proved in error, it would weaken his book and shake public confidence in his law of positivities.

Instead, he built a row of terraces on South Santa Fe Avenue. But collecting rents was tame alongside his boom camp experiences.

The Chicago *Tribune* published an article by Will C. Ferril stating that Barney's quarter of a million had made him the richest colored man in Colorado. It reported that Sanderlin was worth $200,000 and told how Lew Price, the laundryman, had sunk a fortune in founding a Negro newspaper, the Denver *Star*, and lost it all.

Later Price was taken ill; but when he reached the hospital, he refused to go to bed until he had preached his own funeral sermon, whereupon he lay down and died.

Wagoner was far from rich but was doing well. During the eighties he served as deputy sheriff and as bailiff of the district court. In 1884 he had been appointed one of the commissioners of the great Cotton Centennial Exposition at New Orleans. Older than Barney, he was stooped now and used a cane and his jutting chin whiskers were snow white.

In 1892, when Sadie was twenty-nine years old, she married William H. A. Wormley, and Barney and Julia went to Washington for the wedding. It was held in the summer parlor of the famous Wormley Hotel, equipped with furniture from the home of Senator Sumner, who had died in 1874, two years prior to the historic conference at the hotel at which the Tilden-Hayes contest may have been decided.

The Wormley family was and still is probably the most distinguished colored family in the United States. Its family tree includes educators, doctors, and officers of the armed services. One Wormley girl married Congressman H. P. Cheatham, and another an attaché of the French legation.

Barney remembered the prediction of the young banker, Luther Kountze, that some day Denver might boast a population of twenty-five or thirty thousand. Now it was a city of more than 100,000, and its mushroom growth brought about political as well as population shifts.

Barney kept warning the Republican leaders that they could not take the colored vote for granted, and sure enough, when the office-holders forgot their campaign promises in 1893, the Negro vote swung to the Populists. It was a lesson that the Republican leaders long remembered.

Three years after her marriage, Sadie returned to Denver for a visit, bringing her six-year-old stepdaughter, Miriam Wormley, who liked to play with the gold nugget on Barney's watch chain. When grown, she took her master's degree at Columbia and became a noted educator, and her son, Burton, was a major in the army.

In 1893 Barney was prepared to start writing his book, then Congress repealed the silver purchase clause of the Sherman Act, causing the panic that brought an abrupt end to Colorado's prosperity.

In one day seven Denver banks closed their doors. Scores of mining millionaires and speculators found themselves virtually penniless. Some of the state's greatest fortunes were wiped out.

Sanderlin, who had invested in farm and city real estate, lost virtually everything. Barney was hard hit. The break in the price of silver demoralized mining, including his Breckenridge holdings. He lost some money in a bank failure, but there were no mortgages on his real estate.

He owned a two-story business building at 1313 Fifteenth Street, in the heart of the business district, but like most of the store buildings it was standing vacant. To raise ready cash to pay taxes, he started a barber shop again in his vacant property, only two blocks from the spot where he had established his first shop thirty-three years earlier. Forced back into business, he was compelled to postpone work on his book.

In recent years he had made substantial progress with his law of positivities, but some equations having to do with the Hereafter still left him thwarted. Could he but find time to concentrate on these calculations, he was confident that he could work out answers to the important problems dealing with God and the Hereafter.

Across the street from his three-chair shop, a carved wooden figure stood on the sidewalk in front of a tobacco shop. Instead of an Indian, this was the figure of a black Jamaican plantation worker, like the Zambos and Black Caribs of Nicaragua, wearing only a short skirt. The skin of this wooden man was coal black and his left hand held forth a bundle of cigars while his right gripped a machete.

To prevent children from congregating on his corner, the tobacconist told them that this black wooden man was the devil and would devour them unless they kept their distance. Occasionally one of these little shavers would seek refuge in Barney's shop from this devil. Barney would allay their fears with a peppermint stick such as he kept to calm children having their first haircut.

He had always believed not only in an anthropomorphic God, but in a personal devil. He had spent a great deal of time reflecting on the likeness of God, but had wasted little thought on the devil. Now he disliked to think that all these youngsters were to grow up believing the devil to be a black man, identifying colored people with something evil.

But how could he prove that the devil was not black? All the pictures in color showed the devil to be red, with horns and a lashing tail.

As business began to improve, he should have given up his shop and settled down to work on his book, but instead he rented another shop across Seventeenth Street from Denver's newest, largest, and

196

most aristocratic hotel, the Brown Palace, and employed Sanderlin as manager. Then he bought an interest in the Colorado Shirt Manufacturing Company. He had pulled through the panic years in reasonably sound circumstances.

Later he placed a manager in his Fifteenth Street shop and would drive down in his carriage once a day and spend an hour or two at each shop, merely to keep in touch with old-time friends and learn the views of his customers.

In his Fifteenth Street shop the names on the shaving mugs were mostly those of old-timers who had been doing none too well. The mugs in his uptown shop bore the names of prospering Johnny-come-latelys who had moved to Capitol Hill. Barney liked to sit in one shop or the other and talk with the customers. They still came in to hear him quote the classics, and this was good for trade.

Gambler Ed Chase was one of his regulars, and so was William N. Byers when he came to Denver from the mountain home to which he had moved. Byers had served several terms as postmaster but now, getting along in years, was spending most of his time writing a history of Colorado.

Chase had accumulated a tidy fortune but still kept begging Barney to tell him more about his law of positivities, for with such a system the gambling business would be unbeatable. To learn all about it, Barney told him, would cost him only a dollar, for that, he estimated, would be the retail price of his book.

Chase was uncertain whether he was serious, but Barney said yes, he was planning to write down everything in a book just as soon as he could get around to it, explaining just how his system works, with examples.

Chase suggested that it would be a damned shame to let the general public in on it, and if it really worked, he would pay him more for the exclusive rights than any book could possibly bring in.

Barney pointed out that he was comfortably fixed and was uninterested in making a great deal of money from his book; he said he merely wished to help others and make things easier for them.

The gambler was convinced that such a book would prove to be the ruination of mankind. If everyone could calculate in advance what the future held, how could they get any fun out of life, and, besides, what would happen to the gambling business?

What if a man could foretell that lightning was to kill him next summer? Would that help him get along better? No, it would drive him to distraction, and it would all be Barney's fault.

Barney pointed out that Chase was assuming that the law of positivities would do things that he had never claimed for it. He had never claimed that it would tell if someone would be struck by lightning. It was merely a mathematical system for setting down all the known factors to learn from them an unknown factor.

Upon consideration, Chase expressed his disappointment in Barney. No pencil and paper was required to calculate something of that kind. All it demanded was common sense.

So that's what Barney's system amounted to in the end, he decided: merely plain, ordinary, common horse sense — something that he conceded Barney possessed in a high degree.

And all the time he had been deluding people into believing that he possessed some uncanny system for foretelling the future, when all he had was an extraordinary share of plain, God-given intelligence. It was unfair to the public to hint of a mysterious law of positivities when actually all he had was a brain sharper than most. Chase never mentioned the subject again.

His attitude failed to shake Barney's faith in his algebraic system, but he asked himself, what if the general public believes there is nothing to his system but plain horse sense? Why, it would make a fool of him if he came out with a book that was nothing but common sense!

For some time he was discouraged and did no more work on his book. But the more he considered it, the more he became convinced that the gambler was mistaken. After all, what is science but common sense? Take any of the world's great discoveries. Once made, anyone can tell that they are just common sense.

So with his book. He had spent many years working out the answers to his examples. Up to now people could only hope and guess about the Hereafter, but Barney could explain a system by which one could actually know about such things. Wouldn't that be worthwhile?

So what matter if afterwards the public thought it was merely common sense and plain logic? It was what they thought about the work of Galileo and Euclid and Descartes and all the other eminent thinkers.

It appeared that everyone was writing a history of Colorado. In 1895 General Frank Hall published four fat volumes, and the fourth was largely biographies of outstanding pioneers.

Barney's was among the longest — longer even than that of Governor John Evans, twice as long as the biography of Publisher Byers. It failed to mention that Barney was a colored man, but the volume included a picture of him and of his Breckenridge home.

Julia took vast pride in the account and would boast about it and show the book to her friends, and she wrote to her Chicago kinfolk about it, until one day a neighbor told her she was unable to find Barney's picture in the book.

Julia showed her the picture. The neighbor secured a copy of the volume from the public library, and on the page where Barney's picture should have been there appeared the picture of a white man.

Apparently someone had objected to a picture of a Negro in the history, so midway of the edition Barney's picture had been removed and that of the white man substituted.

Although Governor Evans was not accorded as long a biography as Barney's, he was described as a great man who had accomplished much for Colorado, which Barney knew to be true. Evans was a great man, and everyone conceded that he had done more to build the state than anyone except perhaps Dave Moffat, the banker and railroad builder.

Everyone agreed that he was a public-spirited citizen and a good governor and a man whose integrity could not be questioned, with all of which Barney could agree. He did not dislike Evans for his part in the race equality struggle. He felt sorry for him.

Most persons would have felt it strange that a mulatto barber should feel sorry for a rich man, a former governor, one who had helped found Northwestern University and the University of Denver.

Barney believed that Evans had never fully reconciled himself to his failure to win a seat in the United States Senate. Even after he had withdrawn from the race "for the sake of harmony," he had gone about denying that he had ever opposed equal rights for the colored people and reminding listeners of how much he had done for the Underground Railroad before the war. He had even donated $500 to the building fund of each of two Negro churches.

As Barney saw it, deep in his heart Evans had never opposed equal rights. But he was ambitious to win the Senate seat; after all, Colorado had voted ten to one against equal suffrage, and isn't a public official supposed to represent the views of his constituents?

Of course, it had made no difference what the people of Colorado wanted, what counted was the wishes of the equal rights Republican Congress. Barney doubted that the politicians were stupid for failing to grasp the situation. After all, they had no law of positivities by which they could reason out the Unknown and doubtless reasoned that they were advocating the "greatest good of the greatest number." This, Barney knew, was too often an excuse to deny the rights of minorities.

Evans never visited Barney's shops, but John J. Riethmann did. Since he had been Barney's tenant, he had bought a drug store and a great deal of real estate and now was part owner of the street car system and president of the German Bank.

He had always assumed that Barney was a college graduate and could scarce believe his ears when his former landlord disclosed that he had never experienced a day of schoolroom learning. So Barney told him about his life as a slave, and how his black mother had whipped into him the desire for learning. The next time the banker came in for a mustache trim, he said that he had been thinking about Barney's story and had become curious about one phase.

Of a thousand men born in slavery, he claimed, nine hundred and ninety-nine would have turned out to be lazy, shiftless, no-account, ambitionless cotton field niggers. How was Barney different? What had inspired him to accomplish what he had accomplished for himself and for his people?

Knowing the conclusion that any white man would reach, Barney merely smiled and asked him his opinion. He well knew what the answer would be.

Riethmann asserted that of course his white blood had given him the ambition to drive him onward and upward. It is what any white man would believe.

Barney pointed out that he knew any number of mulattoes who were still ambitionless cotton field hands, and this failed to support the banker's theory. And Larimer Street was filled with as many shiftless, lazy whites. No, he could not agree that the color of the skin had any connection with laziness or its lack.

Riethmann then suggested that Barney would attribute his energy, ambition, and intelligence to some of his maternal forbears, some ancestral African chief, perhaps.

Barney said he was absolutely wrong. Given the same environment, a thousand black men would work out about the same as a thousand whites. A certain percentage of each would be ambitious and would accomplish something. It was not a matter of white nature or black nature, but of human nature.

The banker mistakenly took this for boasting, so Barney was forced to explain that in his case he deserved no credit; it all traced back to his black mother. Except for her fierce ambition for her son, except for her indomitable spirit, Barney doubtless would have proved to be merely another cotton field worker.

For some time the banker considered his answer, and when he was shaved and powdered and the apron whisked away, walked from the shop muttering, you could be right, Barney; you could be right.

Although Barney had told him nothing but the truth, he had held something back. He wished that he had dared ask, what if *you* had been born a slave, owned by your own white half-brother? What if he lived in luxury in the Big House and you in a whitewashed slave cabin?

What if life had given him every opportunity that wealth and leisure could bring, and you had not a cent to your name and the law forbade you to learn to read and write?

Knowing that you and your master were sons of the same father, feeling yourself to be fully as intelligent and just as deserving, what would you have done, John J. Riethmann?

And Barney would have answered, you would have done just as I did, balled your fists and resolved that you were just as good a man as he, and by God you were going to prove it to the world!

Claiborne's downfall had been due not only to his own short-comings. The war and the freeing of the slaves had bankrupted thousands like him. Yet, given a spur of ambition such as Barney possessed, he might have overcome his fondness for John Barleycorn, might have made a name for himself as a military or political leader.

It was he, not Barney, who had fallen victim to his environment. It was Claiborne who had suffered from a handicap of birth.

Barney had led the fight for legal and political equality for his people, but social equality cannot be achieved merely by passage of a law. When he had been a power in Colorado politics, and richer, some whites had called on him and had even invited him to their homes, but now that he was out of politics and not so rich, strangely enough most of these white visitors came no more. Perhaps it was because the Fords had been absent from Denver for so many years.

Ever since Denver's first families became wealthy and built mansions on Capitol Hill and developed social ambitions, there had been published an annual Social Register listing the names of the socially elite. The book was the last place where one would expect to find the name of a Negro, but the 1898 edition of the Social Year Book listed the name of Mrs. B. L. Ford.

It was the first and perhaps the last time that the name of a person of color had appeared in the Social Register, and Barney was inordinately proud of the gentle Julia.

XX

When Byers came to Denver, he always visited Barney's uptown shop, where he still kept his shaving mug, to have his beard trimmed. The beard was quite grey now, but his cheeks remained a glowing baby pink.

The two liked to recall old times and the political struggles in which they had engaged, much as might two veterans of the Union and Confederate forces, fighting their battles over without becoming angry, but rather finding rich enjoyment in living over the old days.

Barney was interested in the history that Byers was writing and was hinting about for some advice, and since Byers had been in the printing business he should know all about books.

What if one became absent-minded and misspelled a word; would the publisher print it that way and make the author look foolish, or would he correct it?

Was it true that the publisher bore the expense of printing a book, or was the writer compelled to pay for it?

Were publishers honest, or would they steal your ideas and publish them themselves?

All these questions aroused Byers' curiosity and led him to suspect that Barney was working on a competing history, so Barney told him what he had in mind.

Byers remained unimpressed. Only a student cares to read about algebra; the others have had too much of it crammed down their throats in school. One can't squeeze anything dramatic or exciting or personal out of an equation.

If Barney really wished to try his hand at writing a book, why didn't he write the story of his life? He had lived through some exciting years, and the public likes to read of people leading adventurous lives.

Barney laughed outright, for he had experienced no actual adventures or hairbreadth escapes. And who would be interested in reading about a plain, ordinary, runaway slave who was only a barber? Why, as every editor knows, the public likes to read about kings and knights and nobles!

But Byers argued that he had played a leading part in shaping the history of the state. Twice he had blocked statehood, and except for his support on the last attempt, Colorado might never have become a state.

Hadn't he defeated Governor Evans? Wasn't he known as a President-maker who had elected one President and kept another in office? Wasn't that something to write about?

Barney said he doubted it, even if it were true; he said that it could not be claimed rightly that any one man had accomplished these things.

He had no intention of making a fool of himself with such ridiculous claims. He had something vastly more important to write about than himself, his law of positivities.

Angered, Byers said Barney was becoming foolish in his old age, but the next time he came into the shop he had forgotten his annoyance. He boasted that Barney had accomplished more for the colored race than any man in Colorado. Barney ridiculed the assertion.

Byers branched off to the subject of Ouray, chief of the Ute Indians. What had Ouray done for his people, except sell them out to the whites for a thousand-dollar pension? Yet they placed Ouray's picture in a stained glass window in the statehouse among Colorado's great men, and even named a town for him.

On the other hand, how about Barney Ford, who had fought for his people and won their battle for equal rights and helped build Colorado; did they put his picture in a stained glass window? No, by God, and it was a damned shame, that's what it was!

Considerably wrought up, Byers pointed out that all the monuments were of scouts and generals and politicians who had carved out physical frontiers, which was all very well and they deserved them.

But how about a leader who had fought sixteen years to establish a social frontier that would last forever and protect thousands of citizens against injustice? Why didn't someone erect a monument to him?

Barney held that to be nothing more than idle talk and sought unsuccessfully to calm the former publisher. Byers asked, you know what I'd do, Barney, if I were still publishing the *News*? I'd start a campaign to put your picture up there in a stained glass window in the capitol, along with our other leading pioneers, that's what I'd do!

Barney thanked him for his kind words, but he knew that there was not the slightest chance for a colored man's picture to be placed in the capitol. But he remarked that if Byers had not sold the *News* there was one favor that he would ask of him. He would ask him to start a movement to change the name of Nigger Hill at Breckenridge.

Probably the whites never gave it a thought, but the colored people have no liking for that word "nigger," for it is a contempt word offensive to everyone with a dark skin.

The people of Colorado had grown more tolerant since the sixties, and if the matter could only be brought to their attention, he felt confident that they would do something about it.

The indignant Byers pointed out that Colorado had hundreds of mountain peaks and streams and towns named for Indians who had done nothing for the state. But was there any such evidence of what the colored people had done? Yes, to the everlasting shame of Colorado, there was. Nigger Hill!

Byers was carried away, telling of what he would do if he still owned the *News*. Not only would he get the name of Nigger Hill changed, but he would get it named for Colorado's outstanding colored citizen. He would get it named Ford Hill.

Embarrassed, Barney said it would be ridiculous to name a mountain for a barber. Afterwards, considering what Byers had said, he was compelled to admit that it would be pleasing if something were named for him, so his name would not be forgotten.

But Byers no longer owned the *News,* so all this was nothing but idle talk. He was well aware that no Negro could ever be honored by having a mountain named for him.

But there was another means by which he might be remembered. He could build his own monument. His book would be his memorial. A hundred years hence people would be reading it because it opened the door into the Unknown. It might be one of the greatest books ever written.

Now seventy-two years old, in April of 1899 Julia contracted a heavy cold, developed pneumonia, and died. As Barney stood beside her grave at Riverside Cemetery, his book seemed of little importance. He could not imagine how he was to get along without the gentle Julia, who had nursed him through the fever in Nicaragua and who had waited on table without complaint every time his fortunes had declined.

Now Julia knew the answer to the problem that he was still striving to solve. What difference if he could demonstrate how to learn about the Hereafter? Sooner or later each person found out for himself.

Louis and Sadie returned to Denver for the funeral, but Frankie was ill and unable to leave San Francisco. Sadie begged Barney to return to Washington with her, and he sold the High Street house because he could not bear to live with its memories longer.

The Wormleys lived in a huge house at Hyattsville, Maryland, just outside Washington. Barney spent his time caring for flowers in the greenhouse, in raising Belgian hares, and in telling stories to Miriam and his other step-grandchildren, but he was discontented and resumed work on his algebra because he disliked to leave anything half done.

He was uncertain whether he would go ahead with his book; it all depended upon his ability to work out the final equation. That is what would make it one of the world's greatest books.

Over the years he had worked hundreds of problems proving the exactitude of the law of positivities, but all these had been relatively simple. The final, paramount problem having to do with the Hereafter was vastly more complicated.

In working that early problem about whether he would live to cross the plains and get rich, he had been uncertain of several of the known factors with which to begin the problem.

The Big Problem depended upon sixteen factors, and years ago when he had begun working on it, only two were what might be called known factors. But since the object of his system was to find the unknown, each of these unknown factors in turn became the subject of a new equation. Some of these problems required months to solve, and his penciled figures filled hundreds of pages.

One by one, over the years, he had worked out all but three, so now he had thirteen of the sixteen known factors. When he had all sixteen, it would be quite simple to work out the answer to the Big Problem of the Hereafter. He was confident that then it could be done easily in ten minutes.

The more he worked, the more he sensed that he was racing against time. He was seventy-eight years old, and time was running out on him. At all costs he must gain that last and most important answer in time to complete his book.

To procure the information to work out the three remaining factors, he persuaded himself that he must return to Denver. He was lonesome for his old-time friends and for the scenes of his early struggle to win equality for his people. The excuse he offered Sadie was that he must get back to Denver to settle his affairs.

This time he made his home with Wagoner on Arapahoe Street, bordering the Five Points district. In his eighties, Wagoner was quite feeble, and all the time that Barney could spare from working his problem he spent nursing his old friend. Early in 1901 he established the fourteenth known factor, leaving but two unfound.

When he received word of Frankie's death, he was unable to go to San Francisco for her funeral. His only grandchild, the blue-eyed Edith, was placed in a San Francisco convent school. So now both Julia and Frankie knew the answer to the Big Problem.

He would talk to Wagoner about his law of positivities, but the old man could work up but little interest. He was too near learning the answer at first hand, which he did late in 1901.

Barney still owned his Fifteenth Street property but had sold his home and deeded his row of terraces to Julia's niece, Mrs. Marcelline

Beatty, a nurse, and in return she was to care for him for the remainder of his days.

Following Wagoner's death, Barney lived with this niece in the terrace at 203 Santa Fe Avenue. He would help with the chores when not spending his time with his pencil working on the fifteenth factor.

And then in the middle of the night the answer came to him. Sometimes when he had thought and thought over some problem and it seemed that he was getting nowhere, suddenly the answer would come to him in a flash, usually at night.

Now he was left with but one factor of the sixteen to be worked out before he could sit down and find the answer to the Big Problem in less than ten minutes. He was emotionally stirred, for he was drawing close to his goal and it would be a pity if something happened before he could work out the answer. Think what the world might lose!

But he felt certain that nothing would happen. He was only eighty-one years old and surmised that he was good for some years yet. He was not feeble, as Wagoner had been. He still walked stiffly erect, never using a cane except once after he had slipped and wrenched his back.

He could not sleep as soundly as in years gone by, but actually this was fortunate, for it left him plenty of time to work on that sixteenth factor. Sometimes he would work at his figures until sunrise and then, after breakfast, doze in the rocking chair on the front porch.

When ciphering away at his equation, he would become tremendously enthused, as eager as when first he had reached the Pikes Peak country with the knowledge that he was to become rich.

Each night it seemed that only a few hours more would bring him the answer to that sixteenth factor, and then in another ten minutes he could work out the Big Problem and know all about God and the Hereafter, all about the questions that had been troubling him all his life and leading him to wish and wonder.

But his sixteenth factor was unyielding, and the months kept rolling on. He stored the lawn mower in the coal shed and got out the rake and piled up the dead cottonwood leaves and burned them, and still he could not master that stubborn sixteenth factor.

And then he hung up the rake and got out the snow shovel, but as for the equation, it was still beyond him. He was really pushing himself, now; he felt that at any moment the answer would come to him, as had been the case with factor fifteen, and then it would require but ten minutes or so before he combined the sixteen known factors to get the final answer, the answer to the Big Problem.

After that it would require but little time to prepare his book for the publisher. All but the last chapter had been written and polished and the spelling checked against the dictionary. His manuscript made quite a large bundle, which he kept in his leather-bound trunk in the back bedroom.

In December it set in to snow day after day, but he cared little because he could work better in the quiet of snowy nights. He would sit at the black walnut desk in the front parlor, working and working and stopping only long enough to pick up the scuttle and shoot more coal on the grate fire.

And then one morning just before daylight, it began coming to him, working itself out faster and faster, like a snowball rolling downhill and getting larger and larger.

The closer he came to the answer, the faster came his breath. It was like his experience in French Gulch when he had struck his first color and knew that it was merely a matter of following it until he came to the gold-bearing sandbar.

He became so excited that he pushed too hard and broke the point of his pencil; and when he re-sharpened it, his fingers were so shaky that the penknife slipped and gashed a finger.

It made no difference, for it was a finger on his left hand, and he wrapped his handkerchief about it and went right on with his calculation.

When the sixteenth factor was all worked out he set it down with scrupulous care:

$$(a+bx)^n \frac{d^n y}{dx^n} + A(a+bx)^{n-1} \frac{d^{n-1}y}{dx^{n-1}} + B(a+bx)^{n-2} \frac{d^{n-2}y}{dx^{n-2}} + Ly = X$$

Only one who has struck a pocket of real pay dirt after prospecting for years without luck can grasp Barney's elation as he leaned back and scanned that string of letters and figures.

At first he wanted to jump and shout, but that would have been unkind while Marcelline was still asleep.

And then all at once he felt let down, dragged out. The room seemed oppressive and stuffy. What he needed was a breath of fresh air, so his head would be clear when he took his sixteen known factors and joined them together to solve the Big Problem.

It would be a good time to shovel snow from the sidewalk for Marcelline. When he donned his hat and muffler and overshoes and went to the coal shed for the snow shovel his heart was thumping wildly, for he knew that it would be but a short time before he learned all about God and the Hereafter.

AFTERWORD

Barney L. Ford died at St. Joseph's Hospital December 14, 1902, of a stroke incurred while shoveling snow. He was buried beside Julia at Riverside Cemetery.

Louis and Sadie came to Denver for the funeral, and Louis remained to settle the estate. He died, unmarried, March 10, 1904, and is buried in the family plot.

Barney's blue-eyed granddaughter, Edith, was burned to death when the convent in which she was a student was destroyed by the San Francisco earthquake and fire in 1906. Sarah Ford Wormley died at Washington July 6, 1924.

After Barney's funeral, Sadie and Marcelline found a bundle of old papers in his trunk, but since they contained only a mass of figures, they stuffed them in the kitchen stove and burned them. Sadie preserved her mother's scrap book.

Should the reader care to experiment with the law of positivities and seek the answer to the problem Barney came so close to solving, he can find the basis of the algebraic system outlined in two books listed in the bibliography, written by the distinguished British mathematician, George Boole, and published shortly after Barney made his original discovery.

The gambler, Ed Chase, reached the conclusion that Barney's method was nothing more nor less than a system of logical reasoning or, to use his own words, common sense. Whatever it may be called, it gave him the confidence in himself which beyond doubt contributed to his remarkable accomplishments in the face of seemingly insurmountable difficulties.

The unadorned record of these accomplishments may be found

in public libraries, newspaper files, and state historical societies, but these records fail to disclose the workings of Barney's mind, his thoughts and feelings. This portion of his story has been supplied by the author without, however, in any way distorting or exaggerating his record of accomplishment. The dialogue is the product of the author's imagination.

Since Barney never wrote the story of his life, there exists no record of the workings of Barney's mind or of his heart, but this does not indicate that these phases of the inner man were to remain forever unknown. He had worked out a means to penetrate the Unknown and found that it may be used to learn about the Heretofore as well as the Hereafter. It is of scant importance whether it be called the law of positivities, symbolic logic, logical reasoning, or plain common sense.

It was used by the author to probe the thoughts and feelings of *Mister* Barney Ford. Any errors may be attributed to the lack of known factors at the outset, rather than to the failure of his law of positivities.

F. P.

BIBLIOGRAPHY

ABBOTT, C. "Cheyenne," in *Taming the Frontier*, edited by Duncan Aikman. New York: Minton, Balch & Co., 1925.

BARDWELL, RODNEY J., Jr. "The Territory of Jefferson," in monthly *Brand Book*, October, 1951. Denver: The Westerners.

BEARD, CHARLES A. *American Government and Politics*. New York: Macmillan Co., 1911.

BEEBE, LUCIUS and CLEGG, CHARLES. *The Saga of Wells, Fargo*. New York: E. P. Dutton, 1949.

BOOLE, GEORGE. *An Investigation of The Laws of Thought*. London: Dover Pubs., Inc., 1854.

_____. *Mathematical Analysis of Logic*. London: G. Bell, 1847.

(BRECKENRIDGE, COLO.) Summit County *Journal*, files 1880-90.

(BRECKENRIDGE, COLO.) Summit County *Leader*, Jan. 1, 1881.

BRYCE, JAMES. *American Commonwealth*. New York: Macmillan Co., 1910.

BUCKMASTER, HENRIETTA. *Let My People Go*. New York: Harper & Bros., 1941.

BYERS, WILLIAM N. *History of Colorado*. Chicago: Century Pub. and Eng. Co., 1901.

(CENTRAL CITY, COLO.) Daily *Register-Call*. June 9, 1888.

(CHEYENNE, WYO.) Daily *Leader*. Files, 1867-75.

(CHICAGO) Daily *News*. March 18, 1890.

(CHICAGO) *Inter-ocean*. Sept. 29, 1875.

(CHICAGO) *Journal*. Jan. 27, 1866.

Claim Book, Arazonia Silver Mining District, Breckenridge, Colo., 1860, in files of Colorado State Historical Society, Denver.

Claim Book, Illinois Central Mining District, Central City, Colo., 1864, Gilpin County Clerk and Recorder's Office.

Colorado Directory, 1871.

Colorado Mining Directory. Kansas City: Ramsey, Millet & Hudson, 1883.

Congressional Directory, Forty-fourth Congress, second session.

Congressional *Globe*, Thirty-ninth Congress, first session.

213

DAWSON, T. F. Scrap Book, in files of Colorado State Historical Society, Denver.

Denver City and Auraria in 1860 (Maps). Colorado State Historical Society, 1936.

(DENVER) City Directories, 1877-1902.

(DENVER) Daily *Times.* July 6, 1876, Dec. 16, 1902.

(DENVER) *Gazette.* Jan. 8, 1866.

(DENVER) *Republican.* Dec. 12, 1902.

(DENVER) Rocky Mountain *News.* Files, 1859-1919.

(DENVER) *Social Year Book.* Denver: Carson-Harper Co., 1898.

DILL, ROBERT G. *The Political Campaigns of Colorado.* Denver: Arapahoe Pub. Co., 1895.

DOUGLASS, FREDERICK. *Life and Times of Frederick Douglass.* Boston: De Wolfe & Fisk Co., 1892.

DUNNING, WILLIAM ARCHIBALD. *The American Nation.* New York: Harper & Bros., 1907.

EPPSE, MERL R. *The Negro, Too, in American History.* Nashville: National Publication Co., 1943.

(FAIRPLAY, COLO.) *Flume.* Dec. 7, 1882.

Files, Probate. Denver County Court.

Files, Territorial District Court of Colorado, now in files of District Court, Denver.

FLANDERS, RALPH BETTS. *Plantation Slavery in Georgia.* University of North Carolina Press, 1933.

GREENE, LAURENCE. *The Filibuster — Career of William Walker.* Indianapolis and New York: Bobbs-Merrill Co., 1937.

HAFEN, LeROY R. "Jefferson Territory and Its Competitors," in annual *Brand Book.* Denver: The Westerners, 1945.

HAFEN, LeROY R. and ANN W. *Colorado.* Denver: Old West Pub. Co., 1943.

HALL, FRANK. *History of Colorado,* vols. I-IV. Chicago: Blakely Ptg. Co., 1889-95.

HARVEY, JAMES R. "Negroes in Colorado" in *Colorado Magazine,* July, 1949.

House Executive Documents, vol. 16, Thirty-third Congress, first session.

LANE, WHEATON J. *Commodore Vanderbilt.* New York: Alfred A. Knopf, 1942.

(LARAMIE, WYO.) *Sun.* Nov. 3, 1875.

McGRATH, MARIA DAVIES. *Real Pioneers of Colorado,* vol. II (typescript). Denver: Denver Museum, 1934.

Memorial to The Congress of The United States on Behalf of The Sufferers from The Bombardment and Destruction of Greytown, or San Juan del Norte, by The U. S. Sloop-of-war, *Cyane,* on the 13th of July, A.D. 1854. New York: John A. Gray, 1859.

MILLIGAN, EDWARD D. "Glimpses of Early Denver," in annual *Brand Book*. Denver: The Westerners, 1946.

Minutes, School District No. 1, Arapahoe County, 1862-74. Now in files of School District No. 1, Denver.

Minutes, Society of Colorado Pioneers, 1872-82, in files of Western History Collection, Denver Public Library.

NEFF, ANDREW LOVE. *History of Utah*. Salt Lake City: Deseret News Press, 1940.

(NEW YORK) *Tribune*. July 13, 1859.

OLIPHANT, LAURENCE. "A Run to Nicaragua," in *Blackwood's* Magazine, May, 1857.

Records, Articles of Incorporation, Office of Colorado Secretary of State, Denver.

Records, Colorado State Bureau of Vital Statistics, Denver.

Records, District Court, Summit County, Breckenridge, Colo.

Records, Riverside Cemetery, Denver.

Records, St. Joseph's Hospital, Denver.

Revised Statutes of Colorado, 1868.

ROCHE, JAMES JEFFERSON. *By-ways of War*. Boston: Small, Maynard & Co., 1901.

SIMMONS, The Rev. WILLIAM J. *Men of Mark*. Chicago: George M. Rewell & Co., 1887.

SIMONIN, LOUIS LAURIENT, as translated by Wilson O. Clough. "A French View of Cheyenne," in *Frontier*, March, 1930. Missoula: University of Montana.

SMILEY, JEROME C. *History of Denver*. Denver: Times-Sun Pub. Co., 1901.

——————. *History of Colorado*. Chicago: Lewis Pub. Co., 1913.

SPRING, AGNES WRIGHT. *Cheyenne and Black Hills Stage and Express Routes*. Glendale, Calif.: Arthur H. Clark Co., 1949.

SQUIER, E. GEORGE. *Adventures on The Mosquito Shore*. New York: Worthington Co., 1891.

STILL, WILLIAM. *The Underground Rail Road*. Philadelphia: Porter & Coates, 1872.

STONE, WILBUR F. "Early Pueblo and The Men Who Made It," in *Colorado Magazine*, November, 1929.

TRIGGS, J. H. *History of Cheyenne and Northern Wyoming*. Omaha: Herald Steam Book and Job Printing House, 1876.

VILLARD, OSWALD GARRISON. *John Brown*. Boston and New York: Houghton-Mifflin Co., 1910.

WHITE, The Rev. GEORGE. *Historical Collections of Georgia*. New York: Pudney & Russell, 1855.

WILLIAMS, GEORGE W. *History of The Negro Race in America.* New York: G. P. Putnam's Sons, 1882.

WOODSON, C. G. "The Wormley Family," in *Negro History Bulletin,* January, 1948.

INDEX

217

218